WITHDRAWN

Credit
Management

Workbook

Alison Aplin

BOLTON COLLEGE LIBRARY

Acc. No.	045477
Class No.	657 ALP
Sup.	OSBORNE £7.15
Date	01/17
Site	DR SF LRC

© Alison Aplin, 2016.

All rights reserved. No part of this publication may be reproduced, stored in a retrieval system, or transmitted in any form or by any means, electronic, mechanical, photo-copying, recording or otherwise, without the prior consent of the copyright owners, or in accordance with the provisions of the Copyright, Designs and Patents Act 1988, or under the terms of any licence permitting limited copying issued by the Copyright Licensing Agency, Saffron House, 6-10 Kirby Street, London EC1N 8TS.

Published by Osborne Books Limited
Tel 01905 748071
Email books@osbornebooks.co.uk
Website www.osbornebooks.co.uk

Design by Laura Ingham

Printed by CPI Group (UK) Limited, Croydon, CR0 4YY, on environmentally friendly, acid-free paper from managed forests.

MIX
Paper from responsible sources
FSC® C019777

British Library Cataloguing in Publication Data
A catalogue record for this book is available from the British Library

ISBN 978 1911198 000

Contents

Also available from Osborne Books...

Tutorials

Clear, explanatory books written
precisely to the specifications

Student Zone

Login to access your free ebooks and
interactive revision crosswords

Download **Osborne Books App** free from the App Store or Google Play Store
to view your ebooks online or offline on your mobile or tablet.

www.osbornebooks.co.uk

Introduction

Qualifications covered

This book has been written specifically to cover the Unit 'Credit Management' which is an optional Unit for the following qualifications:

AAT Professional Diploma in Accounting – Level 4

AAT Professional Diploma in Accounting at SCQF – Level 8

This book contains Chapter Activities which provide extra practice material in addition to the activities included in the Osborne Books Tutorial text, and Practice Assessments to prepare the student for the computer based assessments. The latter are based directly on the structure, style and content of the sample assessment material provided by the AAT at www.aat.org.uk.

Suggested answers to the Chapter Activities and Practice Assessments are set out in this book.

Osborne Study and Revision Materials

The materials featured on the previous page are tailored to the needs of students studying this Unit and revising for the assessment. They include:

- **Tutorials:** paperback books with practice activities
- **Student Zone:** access to Osborne Books online resources
- **Osborne Books App:** Osborne Books ebooks for mobiles and tablets

Visit www.osbornebooks.co.uk for details of study and revision resources and access to online material.

Chapter activities

1   Introduction to credit management

1.1   Your business is experiencing difficulty in extracting payment from one of your top company customers with whom your company communicates on a daily basis. Which of the following options is the best way of obtaining up-to-date information about the customer's credit standing?

(a)	Reading trade magazines	
(b)	A search for the company's accounts at Companies House	
(c)	Talking to your colleagues in the sales and accounts departments	

Tick the **one** correct option.

1.2   Management accounts are useful in the assessment of a limited company's credit standing because they provide information about:

(a)	Guarantees given by the directors, share ownership, profitability	
(b)	Management structure, credit insurance cover, bank balance	
(c)	Profitability, credit insurance cover, gearing	
(d)	Liquidity, profitability, sales revenue	

Tick the **one** correct option.

1.3   Information about a company received from a credit reference agency can include:

(a)	Financial accounts, payment history, records of any court proceedings	
(b)	Financial accounts, bank references, directors' bank details	
(c)	Financial accounts, trade references, employee credit histories	

Tick the **one** correct option.

1.4 You are assessing an application for a trading credit limit of £25,000 with one month terms from a new customer, Tufnell Services Limited. You have received the bank reference and two trade references shown below.

You are to read the references, assess them for risk and complete the table below. You are asked to identify the significant wording in each reference which will guide your assessment of the risk involved.

Aurum Bank PLC

status report: **Tufnell Services Limited**

Request: £25,000 trade credit

Report: The capital of this company is fully employed, but we do not consider the directors would enter into any commitment they could not meet.

Response to trade credit enquiry, received from Hensall & Co

Re: Tufnell Limited: £25,000 trade credit, terms one month

We have been trading with this company for two years and allow £15,000 credit per month on 60 day terms. The company very occasionally exceeds the 60 days.

Response to trade credit enquiry, received from R Wagner Associates

Tufnell Limited: £25,000 credit per month

We have been trading with this customer for over six years and now allow them £10,000 credit per month on 60 day terms. The account is usually paid on time.

Reference received	Risk rating			Significant wording
	high	medium	low	
Aurum Bank PLC				
Hensall & Co				
R Wagner Associates				

1.5 Which **one** of the following options is the most useful source of information about a customer's ability to pay invoices on time?

(a)	The customer's Statement of Profit or Loss	
(b)	A credit rating agency	
(c)	Official publications	

Tick the **one** correct option.

1.6 Your business is assessing the credit status of a new customer who has applied for credit terms. Which **one** of the following options is the most useful source of information about the customer's ability to pay invoices on time?

(a)	A search at Companies House for the customer's filed accounts	
(b)	A trade receivables analysis	
(c)	Supplier trade references	

Tick the **one** correct option.

1.7 Your business is assessing the credit status of a new customer who has applied for 30 day credit and a limit of £20,000. You have sent off for a banker's reference. The answer comes back "Should prove good for your figures and purpose." This means:

(a)	The bank is not fully sure and hints that further enquiries should be made	
(b)	The customer is undoubted and a good credit risk	
(c)	No credit should be given	

Tick the **one** correct option.

1.8 Tony has analysed how regularly his credit customers pay him and expects to receive:

70% by the end of the following month

15% by the end of the second month

10% by the end of the third month

The expected sales revenue for the next three months is:

Sales revenue

£

Month 1	50,000
Month 2	56,000
Month 3	60,000

How much are his expected cash receipts in month 4?   £ ⬚

2 Financial analysis of customer accounts

2.1 Set out below and on the next page are the financial statements for Le Ann Limited.

Le Ann Limited: Statement of Profit or Loss

	20-3	20-2
	£000	*£000*
Sales revenue	6,700	6,250
Cost of sales	4,690	4,250
Gross profit	2,010	2,000
Distribution costs	203	185
Administration expenses	1,003	877
Profit from operations	804	938
Finance costs	16	13
Profit before taxation	788	925
Taxation	140	180
Profit for the year	648	745

The above figures include:

20-3 Depreciation £36,000

20-2 Depreciation £28,000

Le Ann Limited: Statement of Financial Position

	20-3	20-2
	£000	£000
ASSETS		
Non-current assets		
Property, plant and equipment	733	583
Current assets		
Inventories	963	873
Trade and other receivables	1,138	1,113
Cash	11	25
	2,112	**2,011**
Total assets	**2,845**	**2,594**
EQUITY AND LIABILITIES		
Equity		
Share capital	1,500	1,500
Retained earnings	359	258
Total equity	**1,859**	**1,758**
Non-current liabilities		
Borrowing	250	150
Current liabilities		
Borrowings	56	76
Trade and other payables	680	610
Total liabilities	**986**	**836**
Total equity and liabilities	**2,845**	**2,594**

(a) Calculate the liquidity key indicators (to two decimal places) for 20-3 and 20-2 for Le Ann Limited:

Le Ann Limited	20-3 Indicator	20-2 Indicator
Current ratio		
Quick ratio		
Trade receivables collection period in days		
Trade payables payment period in days		
Inventory holding period in days		
Working capital cycle days		

(b) Calculate the profitability key indicators (to two decimal places) for 20-3 and 20-2 for Le Ann Limited:

Le Ann Limited	20-3 Indicator	20-2 Indicator
Gross profit margin %		
Operating profit margin %		
Interest cover		
Return on capital employed %		

(c) Calculate the debt and cash flow key indicators (to two decimal places) for 20-3 and 20-2 for Le Ann Limited:

Le Ann Limited	20-3 Indicator	20-2 Indicator
Gearing %		
EBITDA / total debt		

(EBITDA = Earnings before interest, tax, depreciation and amortisation)

2.2 The credit rating (scoring) system below is used to assess the risk of default from credit customers by calculating key indicators (ratios):

Credit rating (scoring) system	Score
Operating profit margin	
Losses	−5
Less than 5%	0
5% and above but less than 10%	5
10% and above but less than 20%	10
20% or more	20
Interest cover	
No cover	−30
Less than 1	−20
1 and above but less than 2	−10
2 and above but less than 4	0
4 or more	10
Liquidity ratio	
Less than 1	−20
1 and above but less than 1.25	−10
1.25 and above but less than 1.5	0
1.5 or more	10
Gearing (total debt / total debt plus equity)	
Less than 25%	20
25% and above but less than 50%	10
50% and above but less than 65%	0
65% and above but less than 75%	−20
75% and above but less than 80%	−40
80% or more	−100

Risk	Aggregate score
Very low risk	Between 60 and 21
Low risk	Between 20 and 1
Medium risk	Between 0 and −24
High risk	Between −25 and −50
Very high risk	Between −50 and −160

(a) Calculate the total credit rating for each year for the company below by completing the ratings columns in the table:

Belfast Cherries Limited	20-3 Indicator	20-3 Rating	20-2 Indicator	20-2 Rating
Operating profit margin %	6%		3.5%	
Interest cover	1.5		None	
Quick ratio	1.1		0.9	
Gearing %	55%		59%	
Total credit rating				

(b) Based on the results of your credit rating and using the table below, recommend whether a requested credit limit should be given to Belfast Cherries Limited.

Tick your chosen option in the table at the bottom of the page.

Rating	Decision
Very low or low risk current year and very low or low risk previous year	Accept
Very low or low risk current year and medium risk previous year	Accept
Very low or low risk current year and high or very high risk previous year	Request latest management accounts and defer decision
Very high risk or high risk current year	Reject
Medium risk current year and medium, low or very low risk previous year	Accept
Medium risk current year and high or very high risk previous year	Request latest management accounts and defer decision

Customer	Decision	
Belfast Cherries Limited	Accept	
	Reject	
	Request latest management accounts and defer decision	

2.3   The following performance indicators have been calculated for Angelic Ltd:

Accounts receivable collection period (days)	87
Accounts payable payment period (days)	65
Inventory holding period (days)	92

The working capital cycle is ☐ days.

3 Granting credit and setting up customer accounts

3.1 Clarke Limited has been trading with Peacock Limited for several years and has, until recently, always paid to terms. Following several late payments Clarke Limited has now contacted Peacock Limited to request an increase in its credit limit from £50,000 to £100,000.

Clarke Limited has supplied the Statement of Profit or Loss and the Statement of Financial Position shown below and on the next page.

Clarke Limited: Statement of Profit or Loss

	20-2	20-1
	£000	£000
Sales revenue	4,705	3,764
Cost of sales	2,087	1,355
Gross profit	2,618	2,409
Distribution costs	329	188
Administration expenses	2,485	1,920
Profit / (loss) from operations	(196)	301
Finance costs	38	20
Profit / (loss) before taxation	(234)	281
Taxation	-	50
Profit / (loss) for the year	(234)	231

Clarke Limited: Statement of Financial Position

	20-2	20-1
	£000	£000
ASSETS		
Non-current assets		
Property, plant and equipment	1,030	1,050
Current assets		
Inventories	240	241
Trade and other receivables	928	619
Cash	-	11
	1,168	871
Total assets	**2,198**	**1,921**
EQUITY AND LIABILITIES		
Equity		
Share capital	850	850
Retained earnings	16	250
Total equity	**866**	**1,100**
Non-current liabilities		
Borrowing	750	650
Current liabilities		
Bank overdraft	159	-
Trade and other payables	423	171
Total liabilities	**1,332**	**821**
Total equity and liabilities	**2,198**	**1,921**

Peacock Limited has calculated financial indicators from the financial statements provided by Clarke Limited.

These indicators are shown at the top of the next page.

Clarke Limited	20-2	20-1
Gross profit margin %	55.64	64
Operating profit margin %	−4.17	8
Interest cover	None	15.05
Current ratio	2.01	5.09
Trade payables payment period in days	73.98	46.06
Trade receivables collection period in days	71.99	60.03
Inventory holding period in days	41.97	64.92
Gearing %	51.21	37.14

The Sales Manager of Peacock Limited has reviewed the financial statements provided by Clarke Limited and the financial indicators shown above and has made some comments.

You are to write bullet point notes dealing with each comment that the Sales Manager has made in (a) to (j) below.

(a) The company turnover has increased by 20% from £3,764,000 to £4,705,000. This is a clear sign of overtrading.

(b) The gross profit has increased, which is a good sign.

(c) The profit from operations has decreased by £196,000. This means that less cash is available to pay debts.

(d) The interest cover has decreased which means that the company is in a worse position than last year.

(e) The current ratio should be 2 which means that last year it was too high.

(f) The trade receivables have increased by 50% which supports the conclusion of overtrading.

(g) The trade payables have increased by £252,000 which indicates the company is not paying its suppliers and requires the increase in the credit limit.

(h) The inventory has remained the same which is a good sign.

(i) The total funding (equity and borrowing) has only increased by £25,000 which is a good sign.

(j) My conclusion is that credit should be given.

3.2   Below is the expected sales revenue for Charles Ltd for the next three months:

	Sales revenue
	£
Month 1	140,000
Month 2	155,000
Month 3	160,000

Charles Ltd predicts that 98% of the sales for month 1 will be paid and 93% of the sales for months 2 and 3 will be paid. The remaining amounts are predicted to be irrecoverable and will be written off.

Calculate the cost to Charles Ltd for the three months of writing off the irrecoverable amounts:

£ [   ]

3.3   Deborah has introduced a 1% discount if customers settle invoices in the same month. All sales are on credit. Deborah estimates that 70% of customers will pay in the month of sale and the remainder in the following month. Deborah's expected sales revenue is:

	Sales revenue
	£
Month 1	94,000
Month 2	98,000

Calculate the expected cash receipts in month 2:

£ [   ]

3.4   Jason's customers currently pay 30 days after the month-end. He is introducing a 3% discount from month 2 if customers settle the invoice in the same month. He predicts that 80% of customers will take advantage of this. Expected sales revenue is:

	Sales revenue
	£
Month 1	40,000
Month 2	42,000
Month 3	41,000

Calculate the cost of introducing the discount:

£ [   ]

4 Customer accounts – legal aspects

4.1 All valid contracts contain the following four elements:

(a)	Offer, acceptance, specific performance, consideration	
(b)	Offer, acceptance, consideration, an intention to create legal relations	
(c)	Offer, acceptance, termination date, implied terms	

Tick the **one** correct option.

4.2 The term 'subject to contract' in relation to a written contract of sale for goods means that:

(a)	The contract has been agreed and signed but the goods have not yet been delivered to the buyer	
(b)	The contract is unsigned but is now binding on the buyer and seller	
(c)	The terms of the contract have not yet been agreed between the parties – there is an ongoing discussion about the price	
(d)	The buyer has agreed in principle to all the terms of the contract but the contract has not yet been drawn up	

Tick the **one** correct option.

4.3   The Consumer Rights Act states that goods sold must be:

(a)	Manufactured to a very high standard	
(b)	As described	
(c)	Of satisfactory quality	
(d)	Sold at the advertised price	

Tick the **two** correct options.

4.4   Which of the following constitutes an acceptance of an offer in contract:

(a)	'I agree to buy goods from you, but I insist on 15% trade discount'	
(b)	'I agree to buy goods from you and will accept your stated terms and conditions'	
(c)	'I agree to buy this property from you, subject to contract'	

Tick the **one** correct option.

4.5   John agrees to buy Mike's car for £1,000. Nothing is set down in writing. John takes possession of the car but then finds that he does not have the money to pay for the car. Magda, John's partner, agrees to pay the £1,000 as she has recently won £5,000 on the Lottery. The car is then sold but turns out to be unroadworthy and only worth £200. John wants to get his money back. The legal position is as follows:

(a)	John cannot sue Mike because the £1,000 consideration was paid by Magda	
(b)	John cannot sue Mike because the £1,000 consideration was greater than the actual value of the car	
(c)	John cannot sue Mike because the contract was not in writing	

Tick the **one** correct option.

4.6   A person who takes legal action in the courts for compensation for a contract where the work has not been completed will seek the remedy of:

(a)	Satisfactory performance	
(b)	Specific performance	
(c)	Repeat performance	

Tick the **one** correct option.

4.7   The Late Payments of Commercial Debts (Interest) Act allows small companies to charge interest to customers who exceed their credit terms and pay late. The interest charge is based on the current bank base rate.

You are to enter in the box below the percentage rate charged.

If the current base rate is 0.5%, the late payment interest rate is ⬚ per cent.

4.8   A customer owes £8,000 (excluding VAT at 20%) and the debt is 75 days late.

You are to calculate the interest charge under the Late Payments of Commercial Debts (Interest) Act to the nearest penny. Enter the figure in the box below. The bank base rate is 0.5%.

£ ⬚

4.9   The following situation is an example of a person who sues for damages:

(a)	A person who takes legal action in the courts for completion of a contract for laying a patio	
(b)	A person who takes legal action in the courts for money compensation for breach of contract	
(c)	A person who seeks compensation in the courts for damaged goods	

Tick the **one** correct option.

4.10 **You are to** enter each of the following words or phrases into the correct box within the text which follows.

satisfactory quality   **intend**   **fit for the purpose**   **delivery**   **described**

The Consumer Rights Act states that any purchaser should expect goods purchased to be of

, as

and

. Title to the goods passes to the purchaser when the

parties to the contract

that it should, normally this will be on

.

4.11 A customer owes £6,000 (including VAT at 20%) and the debt is 67 days late.

You are to calculate the interest charge under the Late Payments of Commercial Debts (Interest) Act to the nearest penny. Enter the figure in the box below. The bank base rate is 1%.

£ [   ]

4.12 Leon is a consultancy firm providing support to Dinsdale Ltd. Leon normally charges £700 per day for support. A contract with Dinsdale Ltd was signed and commenced on 1 January 20-6 for a period of six months with a planned total of 60 days support. The agreed rate was £650 per day subject to a minimum of 55 days support. Dinsdale Ltd decides how many days will be worked in a month.

A total of 35 days support was provided between 1 January 20-6 and 31 March 20-6. The invoiced amount to date is £22,750. During April, May and June 20-6 Leon provided 22 days support.

How much should Leon invoice Dinsdale Ltd for April, May and June 20-6?

£ [   ]

4.13 ABX Ltd is a large client who appears to be facing financial difficulty; you have just overheard a colleague telling his friends in the pub about this.

This is an example of a breach of:

(a)	Integrity	
(b)	Confidentiality	
(c)	Professional behaviour	
(d)	Professional competence and due care	
(e)	Objectivity	

5 Monitoring and controlling customer accounts

5.1   The sales ledger account for Dido Ltd has become corrupted but the following information is available:

Account balance 1 January 20-3:	£78,000
Invoices raised:	10 January 20-3 £45,000 plus VAT at 20%
	12 February 20-3 £26,400 (VAT inclusive)
Credit notes raised:	16 January 20-3 £2,760 (VAT inclusive) subject to a restocking fee of 10%
Bank receipts:	18 January 20-3 £75,240
	26 February 20-3 £45,000

You are to balance the account of Dido Ltd as at 31 January 20-3 and 28 February 20-3.

5.2 You have been provided with the credit control procedures for Singer Limited. Today's date is 31 August 20-3.

Credit control procedures

1. An order for goods is received by email, fax or phone (all phone calls are recorded).

2. Goods are delivered and a goods received note is signed by the customer.

3. The goods received notes are kept in a file in the accounts office.

4. An invoice will be issued on the day after delivery on 30 day terms.

5. An aged analysis of trade receivables is produced weekly.

6. A statement is sent when the account is 7 days overdue.

7. When a debt is 14 days overdue a reminder telephone call is made.

8. When a debt is 21 days overdue a final reminder letter is sent.

9. When a debt is 28 days overdue the account will be put on stop.

10. The debt will either be placed in the hands of a debt collection company or legal proceedings could be instigated if the customer does not respond to calls or letters.

11. The business is credit insured, however insurance is only given for customers once they have a history of trade with the business of at least 12 months and have successfully paid for at least three invoiced amounts. Only 80% of the value of the debt is insured. VAT will be reclaimed from HMRC.

The assistant responsible for credit control has been on sick leave for several months but you have access to the company credit control procedures.

Set out below is an extract from the aged trade receivables analysis at 31 August 20-3.

Customer	Balance £	0 – 30 days £	31 – 60 days £	61 – 90 days £	Over 90 days £
Baritone Ltd	88,800	38,400	50,400		
Bass Ltd	12,720		12,720		
Contralto Ltd	18,000				18,000
Soprano Ltd	17,400				17,400
Tenor Ltd	39,516	34,440		5,076	

You are to identify the most appropriate course of action for each customer based on the information provided. See the next two pages for details of the customers.

Baritone Ltd

The balance on Baritone Ltd's account consists of two invoices. An unallocated payment has been received for £50,400 and posted to the unallocated payment accounts in the purchase ledger. It has now been identified as a receipt from Baritone Ltd.

The action needed is (tick the correct option):

(a)	Credit Baritone Ltd's account with £50,400 and debit unallocated payments with £50,400	
(b)	Debit Baritone Ltd's account with £50,400 and debit unallocated payments with £50,400	
(c)	Credit Baritone Ltd's account with £50,400 and credit unallocated payments with £50,400	
(d)	Debit Baritone Ltd's account with £50,400 and credit unallocated payments with £50,400	

Bass Ltd

The balance on Bass Ltd's account consists of one invoice dated 23 July 20-3.

The action needed is (tick the correct option):

(a)	The account should be put on stop	
(b)	The account is not overdue so no action is required	
(c)	A final reminder letter should be sent on 5 September 20-3	
(d)	A statement should have been sent on 29 August 20-3	

Contralto Ltd

Contralto Ltd has gone into administration. The account is credit insured.

The action needed is (tick the correct option):

(a)	Place the account on stop and contact a debt collection company to deal with processing a claim against Contralto Ltd	
(b)	Contact the insolvency service and register a claim with the credit insurer	
(c)	Contact the insolvency practitioner and register a claim with the credit insurer	
(d)	Contact the insolvency practitioner and make a provision in the accounts	

Soprano Ltd

The account for Soprano Ltd is on stop. Attempts to contact the customer by telephone have been unsuccessful. The account is credit insured.

Complete the sentence below by inserting the correct figures:

Contact the credit insurer to make a claim for £ [   ]

Make a provision for £ [   ]

Claim VAT of £ [   ] from HMRC.

Tenor Ltd

The amount of £5,076 is for one invoice. Tenor Ltd claims that the goods were not received, but there is a signed delivery note on the file.

The action needed is to (tick the correct option):

(a)	Send the original delivery note signed by Tenor Ltd	
(b)	Raise a credit note for £5,076	
(c)	Send a copy of the signed delivery note which was signed by Tenor Ltd	
(d)	Put the account on stop	

5.3 A small business has a large company customer that is very behind with settling its account. What statute will help the seller encourage earlier settlement of invoices?

Tick the **one** appropriate option.

(a)	Consumer Credit Act	
(b)	Late Payment of Commercial Debts (Interest) Act	
(c)	Insolvency Act	

5.4 A business that wishes to use a service which will remove the risk of losses made through customers becoming insolvent is most likely to use which of the following services?

Tick the **one** appropriate option.

(a)	A credit insurance company	
(b)	A credit reference agency	
(c)	A firm of solicitors	

5.5 Tribbiani Ltd is a regular customer of Ross Ltd. During the year Tribbiani Ltd bought from Ross Ltd 495 items which cost £175 each, including VAT at 20%. At the end of the year Tribbiani Ltd's balance of account was £14,438.

The receivables collection period (to the nearest day) is: ☐ days.

5.6 You have been provided with the credit control policy for William Limited. Today's date is 31 May 20-3.

The company's credit control procedures are as follows:

1   An order for goods is received by email, fax or phone (all phone calls are recorded).

2   Goods are delivered and a goods received note is signed by the customer.

3   The goods received notes are kept in a file in the accounts office.

4   An invoice will be issued on the day after delivery on 30 day terms.

5   An aged analysis of trade receivables is produced weekly.

6   A reminder telephone call is made when the debt is 7 days overdue.

7   When a debt is 14 days overdue a letter is sent.

8   When a debt is 28 days overdue the account will be put on stop.

9   The debt will either be placed in the hands of a debt collection company or legal proceedings could be instigated if the customer does not respond to calls or letters.

10   The business is credit insured, but insurance cover is only for customers once they have a history of trade with the business of at least 12 months and have successfully paid for at least three invoiced amounts. Only 80% of the value of the debt is insured. VAT will be reclaimed from HMRC.

The assistant responsible for credit control has been on maternity leave for several months but you have access to the notes she has prepared.

You are to identify the most appropriate course of action for each customer based on the information provided.

(a)   Bronson Ltd

The balance on Bronson Ltd's account is £22,560. This consists of two invoices, one for £12,960 which is not overdue and one for £9,600 which is overdue. An unallocated payment has been received for £9,600 and posted to the unallocated payment accounts in the purchase ledger. It has now been identified as a receipt from Bronson Ltd.

The action needed is to:

(a) Credit Bronson Ltd's account with £9,600 and debit unallocated payments with £9,600	
(b) Debit Bronson Ltd's account with £9,600 and debit unallocated payments with £9,600	
(c) Credit Bronson Ltd's account with £9,600 and credit unallocated payments with £9,600	
(d) Debit Bronson Ltd's account with £9,600 and credit unallocated payments with £9,600	

(b) Rednap Ltd

This new customer placed its first order a few weeks ago. The goods were delivered on 1 May 20-3 and the invoice was issued on 10 May 20-3 on 30 day terms.

The action needed is:

(a)	The account should be put on stop	
(b)	The account is not overdue so no action is required	
(c)	Rednap Ltd should be contacted and an immediate payment requested	
(d)	A phone call should have been made on 17 May 20-3 and a letter sent on 24 May 20-3	

(c) Hathaway Ltd

A balance of £17,400 is 68 days overdue and is for one invoice. Hathaway Ltd claims that the goods were not received.

The action needed is to:

(a)	Send the original delivery note signed by Hathaway Ltd	
(b)	Raise a credit note for £17,400	
(c)	Send a copy of the signed delivery note which was signed by Hathaway Ltd	
(d)	Send a copy of the signed delivery note signed by the courier who delivered the package	

(d) Winslet Ltd

Winslet Ltd sent a payment of £11,400 but did not provide details of the invoices to which the payment relates.

The action needed is:

(a)	Winslet Ltd should be contacted to confirm which invoices are being paid so that the unallocated receipt can be allocated	
(b)	The £11,400 should be returned to Winslet Ltd	
(c)	The £11,400 should be allocated to the last invoice first	
(d)	The £11,400 should be posted to unallocated payments	

(e) **Taylor Ltd**

Taylor Ltd has gone into administration after being a customer for five years. Up until six months ago, the company had always complied with its credit terms.

The action needed is to:

(a)	Place the account on stop and contact a debt collection company to deal with processing a claim against Taylor Ltd	
(b)	Contact the insolvency service and register a claim with the credit insurer	
(c)	Visit the premises of Taylor Ltd and seize goods to the value of the outstanding balance	
(d)	Contact the insolvency practitioner and register a claim with the credit insurer	

5.7 A business wanting to employ an independent company to help with the running of its Sales Ledger and the issue of invoices is most likely to use the following service:

(a)	Factoring	
(b)	Invoice discounting	
(c)	Credit insurance	

Tick the appropriate option.

5.8 You have been provided with the credit control policy for Barlow Limited. Today's date is 30 April 20-3.

The credit control management procedures are as follows:

1   An order for goods is received by email, fax or phone (all phone calls are recorded).

2   Goods are delivered and a goods received note is signed by the customer.

3   The goods received notes are kept in a file in the accounts office.

4   An invoice will be issued on the day after delivery on 30 day terms.

5   An aged analysis of trade receivables is produced weekly.

6   A reminder telephone call is made when the debt is 7 days overdue.

7   When a debt is 14 days overdue a letter is sent.

8   When a debt is 28 days overdue the account will be put on stop.

9   The debt will either be placed in the hands of a debt collection company or legal proceedings could be instigated if the customer does not respond to calls or letters.

10   The business is credit insured, however insurance is only given for customers once they have a history of trade with the business of at least 12 months and have successfully paid for at least three invoiced amounts. Only 80% of the value of the debt is insured. VAT will be reclaimed from HMRC.

The assistant responsible for credit control has been on secondment to an associate company for several months but you have access to the notes she prepared.

Identify the most appropriate course of action for each customer based on the information provided.

(a)   Tilsley Ltd

Tilsley Ltd has a history of paying late but they have always paid eventually. There is a balance on the account of £20,700 which relates to one invoice dated 1 March 20-3.

The action needed is:

(a) The account should be put on stop	
(b) The account is not overdue so no action is required	
(c) Tilsley Ltd should be contacted and an immediate payment requested	
(d) A statement should be sent on 7 May 20-3	

(b)   Cole Ltd

This new customer placed its first order a few weeks ago. The goods were delivered on 1 April 20-3 and the invoice was raised on 12 April 20-3 on 30 day terms.

The action needed is:

(a) The account should be put on stop	
(b) The account is not overdue so no action is required	
(c) Cole Ltd should be contacted and an immediate payment requested	
(d) A statement should have been sent on 19 April 20-3	

(c)   McDonald Ltd

McDonald Ltd has gone into administration. The account is not credit insured.

The action needed is to:

(a) Place the account on stop and contact a debt collection company to deal with processing a claim against McDonald Ltd	
(b) Contact the insolvency service and register a claim with the credit insurer	
(c) Contact the insolvency practitioner and register a claim with the credit insurer	
(d) Contact the insolvency practitioner and make a provision in the accounts	

(d)   Lloyd Ltd

Lloyd Ltd sent a payment of £7,476 but did not provide details of which invoices relate to the payment.

The action needed is:

(a) Lloyd Ltd should be contacted to confirm which invoices are being paid so that the unallocated receipt can be allocated	
(b) The £7,476 should be returned to Lloyd Ltd	
(c) The £7,476 should be allocated to the last invoice first	
(d) The account should be put on stop until the payment is allocated	

(e) **Duckworth Ltd**

Duckworth Ltd is a long-established customer with a history of late payments, but it always pays eventually. Duckworth Ltd has an overdue balance of £17,000 due to Barlow Ltd.

The Managing Director of Duckworth Ltd is a personal friend of Barlow Ltd's Managing Director.

The action needed is to:

(a)	Place the account on stop and contact a debt collection company to deal with processing a claim against Duckworth Ltd	
(b)	Ask the Managing Director of Barlow Ltd what action should be taken	
(c)	Visit the premises of Duckworth Ltd and seize goods to the value of the outstanding balance	
(d)	Put a claim in to the credit insurance company for the overdue amount	

5.9 A business wanting to encourage a good customer who is also a bad payer to pay up is most likely to:

(a)	Put the account on stop	
(b)	Reduce the customer's credit limit	
(c)	Contact the customer by telephone to discuss the matter	

Tick **one** option.

5.10 Alliance Ltd has total receivables ledger balances of £1,800,000, including £80,000 of debts over 90 days old.

MP Financial can provide Alliance Ltd with a recourse factoring facility. MP Financial will manage the receivables ledger up to a maximum of £1,400,000, or 70% of the outstanding receivables (excluding debts over 90 days old).

Alliance Ltd can borrow £ [   ] immediately.

6 Collecting debts and dealing with insolvency

6.1 A business has a £35,000 debt outstanding on a customer account. Which County Court process deals with this size of debt?

Tick the **one** correct option.

(a)	Small Claims Track	
(b)	Fast Track	
(c)	Multi Track	

6.2 An attachment of earnings is:

Tick the **one** correct option.

(a)	An order for the court bailiffs to enter the property of the customer who owes money to the seller to seize valuable assets	
(b)	An order which will authorise an employer to deduct regular amounts from the customer's salary in order to repay the debt	
(c)	An order which will give the seller a right to the sale proceeds of property owned by the customer	

6.3 A statutory demand made on a trade receivable for an outstanding debt for a sole trader should be for a minimum of:

Tick the **one** correct option.

(a)	£5,000	
(b)	£750	
(c)	£1,000	

6.4 A 'retention of title' clause in a sales contract for goods supplied means that a business that has sold goods but not received payment for them can recover the goods if the buyer becomes insolvent. But the clause will only operate under certain conditions.

Which of the following situations will allow a seller which has incorporated a retention of title clause in its contract to recover the goods?

Tick the **one** correct option.

(a)	The goods can be identified as having been supplied by the seller, for example with a stamp or label	
(b)	The goods have been used in a manufacturing process and mixed with other products	
(c)	The goods have been in the possession of the buyer for less than 60 days	

6.5 You work in the Credit Control Section for Lewis Enterprises, which is owed £10,000 by Brodey Ltd, which has recently been put into liquidation. Brodey Ltd's trade payables total £250,000.

You receive a schedule from the court stating that £500,000 has been realised from the sale of the company's assets. The payables that will receive payment from this are:

Payables to be paid **in full** are:

Liquidation costs and preferential payables	£150,000
Bank floating charge	£200,000

You are to calculate:

(1) The dividend (pence per £1) payable to the trade payables: ☐ pence.

(2) The amount that will be received by Lewis Enterprises: £ ☐

(3) The amount that will be written off as an irrecoverable debt: £ ☐

Ignore any VAT.

6.6 An understanding of insolvency involves the use of very specific terminology. The term 'liquidation' is used in relation to:

(a)	A sole trader	
(b)	A limited company	
(c)	An unincorporated partnership	

Tick the **one** correct option.

6.7 An understanding of insolvency involves the use of very specific terminology. The term 'bankruptcy' is used in relation to:

(a)	A sole trader	
(b)	A private limited company	
(c)	A public limited company	

Tick the **one** correct option.

6.8 A warrant of delivery is:

(a)	An order for the court bailiffs to enter the property of the customer who owes money to the seller to seize valuable assets	
(b)	An order which will authorise an employer to deduct regular amounts from the customer's salary in order to repay the debt	
(c)	An order for the court bailiffs to seize goods belonging to the seller and held by a customer who owes money to the seller	

Tick the **one** correct option.

6.9 A statutory demand is:

(a)	A court order for the repayment of a debt	
(b)	A request by the court to attend a bankruptcy hearing	
(c)	A formal demand for at least £5,000 made by the person or company owed money and issued to an individual	

Tick the **one** correct option.

6.10 A bankruptcy order can be issued by the court against:

(a)	An individual	
(b)	A private limited company	
(c)	A public limited company	

Tick the **one** correct option.

6.11 Kathryn has received a letter from the liquidator of Olive Ltd. Kathryn is owed £6,100 by Olive Ltd. The letter states that all unsecured creditors of Olive Ltd will receive a dividend of 24.64p in the pound.

Calculate the amount that Kathryn should receive:

£ [   ]

Answers to chapter activities

1 Introduction to credit management

1.1 (c) Talking to your colleagues in the sales and accounts departments

1.2 (d) Liquidity, profitability, sales revenue

1.3 (a) Financial accounts, payment history, records of any court proceedings

1.4

Reference received	Risk rating			Significant wording
	high	**medium**	**low**	
Aurum Bank PLC	✔			The capital of this company is **fully** employed.
Hensall & Co		✔		**very occasionally** exceeds
R Wagner Associates		✔		The account is **usually** paid on time.

1.5 (b) A credit rating agency

1.6 (c) Supplier trade references

1.7 (a) The bank is not fully sure and hints that further enquiries should be made

1.8 £55,400

Workings: (£60,000 x 70%) + (£56,000 x 15%) + (£50,000 x 10%)

2   Financial analysis of customer accounts

2.1   (a)

Le Ann Limited	20-3	20-2
	Indicator	Indicator
Current ratio	2.87	2.93
Quick ratio	1.56	1.66
Trade receivables collection period in days	62	65
Trade payables payment period in days	52.92	52.39
Inventory holding period in days	74.95	74.98
Working capital cycle days	84.03	87.59

Workings:

	Formula	20-3	20-2
Current ratio	$\dfrac{\text{Current assets}}{\text{Current liabilities}}$	$\dfrac{2,112}{56 + 680} = 2.87$	$\dfrac{2,011}{76 + 610} = 2.93$
Quick ratio	$\dfrac{\text{Current assets less inventories}}{\text{Current liabilities}}$	$\dfrac{2,112 - 963}{56 + 680} = 1.56$	$\dfrac{2,011 - 873}{76 + 610} = 1.66$
Trade receivables collection period in days	$\dfrac{\text{Trade receivables} \times 365}{\text{Sales revenue}}$	$\dfrac{1,138 \times 365}{6,700} = 62$	$\dfrac{1,113 \times 365}{6,250} = 65$
Trade payables pmt period in days	$\dfrac{\text{Trade payables} \times 365}{\text{Cost of sales}}$	$\dfrac{680 \times 365}{4,690} = 52.92$	$\dfrac{610 \times 365}{4,250} = 52.39$
Inventory holding period in days	$\dfrac{\text{Inventories} \times 365}{\text{Cost of sales}}$	$\dfrac{963 \times 365}{4,690} = 74.95$	$\dfrac{873 \times 365}{4,250} = 74.98$
Working capital cycle days		$74.95 + 62 - 52.92$ $= 84.03$	$74.98 + 65 - 52.39$ $= 87.59$

(b)

Le Ann Limited	20-3 Indicator	20-2 Indicator
Gross profit margin %	30	32
Operating profit margin %	12	15.01
Interest cover	50.25	72.15
Return on capital employed %	38.12	49.16

Workings:

	Formula	20-3	20-2
Gross profit margin %	$\dfrac{\text{Gross profit} \times 100}{\text{Sales revenue}}$	$\dfrac{2,010 \times 100}{6,700} = 30\%$	$\dfrac{2,000 \times 100}{6,250} = 32\%$
Operating profit margin %	$\dfrac{\text{Profit from operations} \times 100}{\text{Sales revenue}}$	$\dfrac{804 \times 100}{6,700} = 12\%$	$\dfrac{938 \times 100}{6,250} = 15.01\%$
Interest cover	$\dfrac{\text{Profit from operations}}{\text{Interest payable}}$	$\dfrac{804}{16} = 50.25$	$\dfrac{938}{13} = 72.15$
Return on capital employed %	$\dfrac{\text{Profit from operations} \times 100}{\text{Net assets}}$	$\dfrac{804 \times 100}{2,845 - 736} = 38.12\%$	$\dfrac{938 \times 100}{2,594 - 686} = 49.16\%$

(c)

Le Ann Limited	20-3 Indicator	20-2 Indicator
Gearing %	14.13	11.39
EBITDA / total debt	2.75	4.27

Workings:

	Formula	20-3	20-2
Gearing %	$\dfrac{\text{Total debt} \times 100}{\text{Total debt plus equity}}$	$\dfrac{306 \times 100}{306 + 1,859} = 14.13\%$	$\dfrac{226 \times 100}{226 + 1,758} = 11.39\%$
EBITDA / total debt	$\dfrac{\text{EBITDA}}{\text{Total debt}}$	$\dfrac{804 + 36}{56 + 250} = 2.75$	$\dfrac{938 + 28}{150 + 76} = 4.27$

2.2   **(a)**

Belfast Cherries Limited	20-3 Indicator	20-3 Rating	20-2 Indicator	20-2 Rating
Operating profit margin %	6%	5	3.5%	0
Interest cover	1.5	−10	None	−30
Quick ratio	1.1	−10	0.9	−20
Gearing %	55%	0	59%	0
Total credit rating		−15		−50

(b)   Request latest management accounts and defer decision

2.3   The working capital cycle is **114** days.

Workings: 87 + 92 − 65 = 114

3 Granting credit and setting up customer accounts

3.1 (a) The company turnover has increased by 20% from £3,764,000 to £4,705,000. This is a clear sign of overtrading.

- It is correct that the turnover has increased; however, the increase is 25% (£941,000 / £3,764,000) not 20%.

- The fact that turnover has increased may be a sign of overtrading, but other factors must be taken into consideration.

- Other indicators of overtrading include reduced profit margins, increased levels of current assets and trade cycle days and the reduction in cashflow.

(b) The gross profit has increased, which is a good sign.

- There has been an increase in gross profit from £2,409,000 to £2,618,000; however the gross profit margin has fallen from 64% to 55.64%, which is not a good sign.

- The fall in the gross profit margin may indicate that suppliers have increased their prices or the company is not taking advantage of prompt payment discounts on offer. It may also indicate that the company has reduced its prices.

(c) The profit from operations has decreased by £196,000. This means that less cash is available to pay debts.

- The profit from operations has decreased and is now an operating loss, it has fallen by £497,000, not £196,000.

- There has been a fall in the operating profit margin of 12.17% (8% + 4.17%).

- This fall is partly due to the fall in the gross profit margin and partly due to an increase in both distribution and administration costs.

- This may not mean that less cash is available to pay debts; it depends on where the profits have gone in the period.

- It is necessary to consider the liquidity of the business and the changes in assets and liabilities.

- There has been an increase in both current assets and liabilities, which may indicate that profits have been tied up in the short-term working capital.

- There has been no investment in non-current assets.

(d) The interest cover has decreased which means that the company is in a worse position than last year.

- The interest cover has decreased from 15.05 times to no cover at all.

- The generation of cash is required to pay interest, and the overall cash balance (including overdraft) has fallen by £170,000, which confirms that the company is in a worse position than in the previous year.

(e) **The current ratio should be 2 which means that last year it was too high.**

- Referring to the fact that the current ratio should be 2 is a common misunderstanding; the level of an 'acceptable' ratio very much depends on the organisation itself and the type of industry to which it belongs.

- The higher the current ratio the better when carrying out credit assessment.

- The current ratio is a simple measure of solvency and it has fallen significantly in this case from 5.09 to 2.01.

- The component parts of the current assets need to be looked at to determine liquidity.

- The cash balance has been converted to a bank overdraft which is worrying and the trade receivables have increased (see below).

(f) **The trade receivables have increased by 50% which supports the conclusion of overtrading.**

- Trade receivables have increased from £619,000 to £928,000 and an increase would be expected with an increase in sales.

- Whether or not this supports overtrading depends on other factors.

- The trade receivables collection period has increased from 60.03 days to 71.99 days. This would indicate that the company is struggling with its credit control procedures and points to overtrading.

(g) **The trade payables have increased by £252,000 which indicates the company is not paying its suppliers and requires the increase in the credit limit.**

- Trade payables have increased significantly and the trade payables payment period has increased by 27.92 days.

- The increase is not a good sign, it indicates that the company is struggling to pay its suppliers on time and also points to overtrading.

- This would appear to be the reason why the company has requested an increase in the credit limit and a similar request has possibly been made to other suppliers.

(h) **The inventory has remained the same which is a good sign.**

- The inventory levels have remained the same, but with a significant increase in turnover an increase in inventory would usually be expected.

- The inventory holding period has fallen by 22.95 days.

- This may indicate that the business is unable to buy further inventory and inventory may run out.

- Or, it may indicate that the business is handling its inventory levels more efficiently.

(i) **The total funding (equity and borrowing) has only increased by £25,000 which is a good sign.**

- The total of equity and borrowing was £1,750,000 and has increased by £25,000 to £1,775,000.

- This is not a good sign because the gearing percentage has increased from 37.14% to 51.21%.

- There has been an increase in both long-term and short-term borrowing and the company is placing a much heavier reliance on borrowing, especially with the introduction of a short-term bank overdraft.

- The bank overdraft and increase in the long-term loan has been used to fund the working capital of the business, as mentioned previously there has been no investment in non-current assets.

(j)   **My conclusion is that credit should be given.**

- Credit should not be given.

- It appears that the company is overtrading and is struggling to pay suppliers on time.

- Long-term and short-term loans have been used to fund the working capital of the business.

3.2   £24,850

Workings: (£140,000 x 2%) + (£155,000 x 7%) + (£160,000 x 7%)

3.3   £96,114

Workings: (£94,000 x 30%) + (£98,000 x 70% x 99%)

3.4   £1,992

Workings: ((£42,000 + £41,000) x 3% x 80%)

4 Customer accounts – legal aspects

4.1 (b) Offer, acceptance, consideration, an intention to create legal relations

4.2 (d) The buyer has agreed in principle to all the terms of the contract but the contract has not yet been drawn up

4.3 (b) As described

(c) Of satisfactory quality

4.4 (b) 'I agree to buy goods from you and will accept your stated terms and conditions'

4.5 (a) John cannot sue Mike because the £1,000 consideration was paid by Magda

4.6 (b) Specific performance

4.7 8.5 per cent

4.8 £167.67

Workings: 9,600 x 8.5% x (75/365)

4.9 (b) A person who takes legal action in the courts for money compensation for breach of contract

4.10 The Consumer Rights Act states that any purchaser should expect goods purchased to be of **satisfactory quality**, as **described** and **fit for the purpose**. Title to the goods passes to the purchaser when the parties to the contract **intend** that it should, normally this will be on **delivery**.

4.11 £99.12

Workings: £6,000 x (8% + 1%) x 67/365

4.12 £14,300

Workings: £650 x 22

4.13 (b) Confidentiality

5 Monitoring and controlling customer accounts

5.1   Balance at 31 January 20-3 = £54,276

Balance at 28 February 20-3 = £35,676

Note that the question asks for a calculation of the balances of the account at the end of the two months. This may either be carried out as a straight arithmetic exercise, or it can be done by completing two double-entry accounts as shown below.

		£			£
1 Jan	B/fwd	78,000			
10 Jan	Invoice	54,000	16 Jan	Credit Note	2,484
			18 Jan	Bank	75,240
			31 Jan	C/fwd	54,276
		132,000			132,000

		£			£
1 Feb	B/fwd	54,276			
12 Feb	Invoice	26,400	26 Feb	Bank	45,000
			28 Feb	C/fwd	35,676
		80,676			80,676

5.2   **Baritone Ltd**   (a)   Credit Baritone Ltd's account with £50,400 and debit unallocated payments with £50,400

Bass Ltd   (d)   A statement should have been sent on 29 August 20-3

Contralto Ltd   (c)   Contact the insolvency practitioner and register a claim with the credit insurer

Soprano Ltd   Contact the credit insurer to make a claim for **£11,600**, make a provision for **£2,900** and claim VAT of **£2,900** from HMRC.

Tenor Ltd   (c)   Send a copy of the signed delivery note which was signed by Tenor Ltd

5.3   (b)   Late Payment of Commercial Debts (Interest) Act

5.4   (a)   A credit insurance company

5.5   **61** days.

Working: $\dfrac{14,438}{86,625} \times 365$

5.6 **(a)** **Bronson Ltd**

(a) Credit Bronson Ltd's account with £9,600 and debit unallocated payments with £9,600

(b) **Rednap Ltd**

(b) The account is not overdue so no action is required

(c) **Hathaway Ltd**

(c) Send a copy of the signed delivery note which was signed by Hathaway Ltd

(d) **Winslet Ltd**

(a) Winslet Ltd should be contacted to confirm which invoices are being paid so that the unallocated receipt can be allocated

(e) **Taylor Ltd**

(d) Contact the insolvency practitioner and register a claim with the credit insurer

5.7 (a) Factoring

5.8 **(a)** **Tilsley Ltd**

(a) The account should be put on stop

(b) **Cole Ltd**

(b) The account is not overdue so no action is required

(c) **McDonald Ltd**

(d) Contact the insolvency practitioner and make a provision in the accounts

(d) **Lloyd Ltd**

(a) Lloyd Ltd should be contacted to confirm which invoices are being paid so that the unallocated receipt can be allocated

(e) **Duckworth Ltd**

(b) Ask the Managing Director of Barlow Ltd what action should be taken

5.9 (c) Contact the customer by telephone to discuss the matter

5.10 Alliance Ltd can borrow £1,204,000 immediately.

Workings: (£1,800,000 – £80,000) x 70%

6 Collecting debts and dealing with insolvency

6.1   (c)   Multi Track

6.2   (b)   An order which will authorise an employer to deduct regular amounts from the customer's salary in order to repay the debt

6.3   (a)   £5,000

6.4   (a)   The goods can be identified as having been supplied by the seller, for example with a stamp or label

6.5   **(1)**   The dividend (pence per £1) payable to the trade payables: 60p

     (2)   The amount that will be received by Lewis Enterprises: £6,000

     (3)   The amount that will be written off as an irrecoverable debt: £4,000

Workings:

(1)   £150K available for trade payables (£500K − £350K) ÷ £250K = 60p

(2)   Dividend to Lewis Enterprises £10,000 x 60p = £6,000

(3)   £4,000 (£10K balance − £6K dividend paid)

6.6   (b)   A limited company

6.7   (a)   A sole trader

6.8   (c)   An order for the court bailiffs to seize goods belonging to the seller and held by a customer who owes money to the seller

6.9   (c)   A formal demand for at least £5,000 made by the person or company owed money and issued to an individual

6.10   (a)   An individual

6.11   £1,503.04

Workings: £6,100 x 0.2464

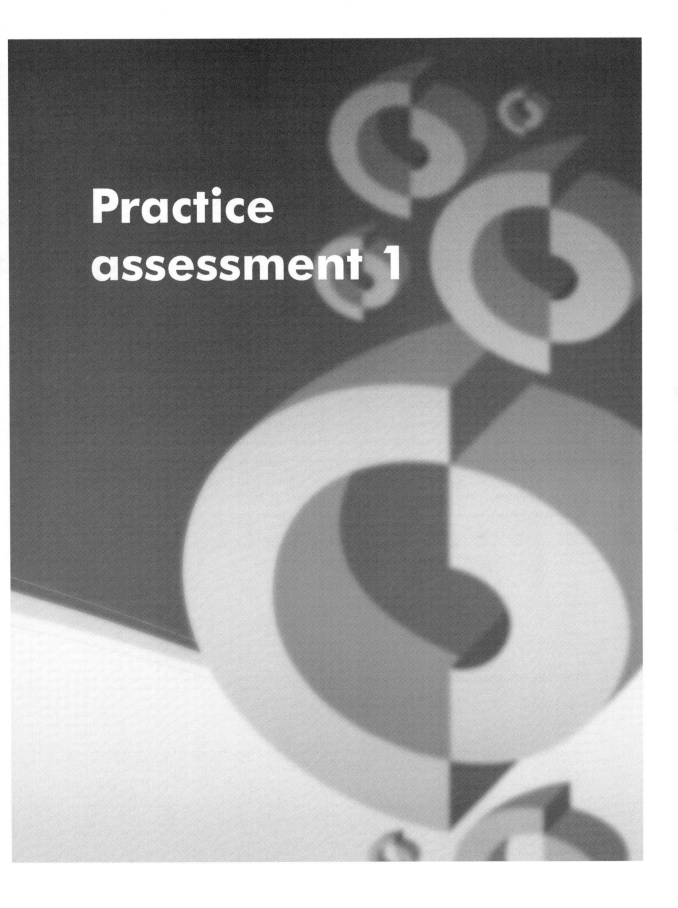

Practice assessment 1

Task 1

(a)   Select the correct words to complete the following statements:

An offer in relation to a contract sale can be made [   ] .

A valid contract must contain these four elements:

[   ]   [   ]   [   ]   [   ]

A shop has set up a notice board where customers can advertise goods or services for sale to the

public. These adverts constitute in contract law an [   ] .

offer	only by the buyer	consideration
guarantee	intention to create legal relations	only by the seller
by the buyer or seller	acceptance	invitation to treat

(b)   A customer owes £5,000 (excluding VAT at 20%) and the debt is 45 days late.

You are to calculate the interest charge under the Late Payments of Commercial Debts (Interest) Act to the nearest penny. Enter the figure in the box below. The bank base rate is 0.5%.

£ [   ]

(c)   **You are to** enter each of the following words into the correct box within the text which follows.

individuals   **companies**   **manual**   **principles**

The Data Protection Act protects data held about [   ] and not

[   ] . It covers both computer-based and [   ]

records. It is based around eight guiding [   ] which protect the data held.

(d)   Bella decides that she wants to sell her car, a classic Porsche, for £40,000. She puts a notice quoting this price in a specialist magazine. She receives an email from an enthusiastic buyer offering her £39,500 for the car. In contract this email is:

(a)	An acceptance	
(b)	Consideration	
(c)	An offer	

Tick the **one** correct option.

A breach of contract occurs when:

(a)	The contract has not been signed	
(b)	The contract is signed by a person not authorised to sign it	
(c)	The terms of the contract are not fulfilled	

Tick the **one** correct option.

(e)   The Consumer Rights Act states that goods sold must be:

Select True or False.

		True	**False**
(a)	Of satisfactory quality		
(b)	Of acceptable quality		
(c)	Fit for the purpose		
(d)	Guaranteed for 12 months		

Task 2

You work as a Credit Control Manager for Lawson Ltd which uses a credit rating system to assess the credit status of new customers. The credit rating (scoring) system is used to assess the risk of default by calculating key indicators (ratios), comparing them to the table and calculating an aggregate score. This system is set out below.

Credit rating (scoring) system	Score
Operating profit margin	
Losses	−5
Less than 5%	0
5% and above but less than 10%	5
10% and above but less than 20%	10
20% or more	20
Interest cover	
No cover	−30
Less than 1	−20
1 and above but less than 2	−10
2 and above but less than 4	0
4 or more	10
Liquidity ratio − quick ratio	
Less than 1	−20
1 and above but less than 1.25	−10
1.25 and above but less than 1.5	0
1.5 or more	10
Gearing (total debt / total debt plus equity)	
Less than 25%	20
25% and above but less than 50%	10
50% and above but less than 65%	0
65% and above but less than 75%	−20
75% and above but less than 80%	−40
80% or more	−100

Risk	Aggregate score
Very low risk	Between 60 and 21
Low risk	Between 20 and 1
Medium risk	Between 0 and −24
High risk	Between −25 and −50
Very high risk	Between −50 and −160

The Sales Department has asked for a credit limit of £45,000 to be given to Sunny Limited, a potential new customer. The financial information below has been supplied by Sunny Limited.

Sunny Limited: Statement of Profit or Loss

	20-3	20-2
	£000	£000
Sales revenue	4,200	3,850
Cost of sales	2,495	2,329
Gross profit	1,705	1,521
Distribution costs	206	147
Administration expenses	869	604
Profit from operations	630	770
Finance costs	36	77
Profit before taxation	594	693
Taxation	120	150
Profit for the year	474	543

Sunny Limited: Statement of Financial Position

	20-3	20-2
	£000	£000
ASSETS		
Non-current assets		
Property, plant and equipment	1,832	1,846
Current assets		
Inventories	68	54
Trade and other receivables	450	650
Cash	1,350	1,450
	1,868	2,154
Total assets	3,700	4,000
EQUITY AND LIABILITIES		
Equity		
Share capital	1,200	1,000
Retained earnings	525	450
Total equity	1,725	1,450
Non-current liabilities		
Borrowing	850	1,050
Current liabilities		
Borrowings	380	505
Trade and other payables	745	995
Total liabilities	1,975	2,550
Total equity and liabilities	3,700	4,000

(a)   Complete the table below by calculating the key indicators (to two decimal places) for 20-3 and 20-2 for Sunny Limited, and rate the company using the credit rating scoring system.

Sunny Limited	20-3 Indicator	20-3 Rating	20-2 Indicator	20-2 Rating
Operating profit margin %				
Interest cover				
Quick ratio				
Gearing %				
Total credit rating				

(b) Based on the results of your credit rating and using the table below, recommend whether the requested credit limit should be given to Sunny Limited.

Rating	Decision
Very low or low risk current year and very low or low risk previous year	Accept
Very low or low risk current year and medium risk previous year	Accept
Very low or low risk current year and high or very high risk previous year	Request latest management accounts and defer decision
Very high risk or high risk current year	Reject
Medium risk current year and medium, low or very low risk previous year	Accept
Medium risk current year and high or very high risk previous year	Request latest management accounts and defer decision

Credit decision	
(a) Accept	
(b) Reject	
(c) Request latest management accounts and defer decision	

Task 3

James Limited has been trading with Lawson Limited for several years and has, until recently, always complied with its credit terms. Following several late payments James Limited contacted Lawson Limited to request an increase in its credit limit from £30,000 to £60,000. James Limited has supplied the Statement of Profit or Loss below and the Statement of Financial Position on the next page.

James Limited: Statement of Profit or Loss

	20-2	20-1
	£000	£000
Sales revenue	5,988	4,785
Cost of sales	3,293	2,631
Gross profit	2,695	2,154
Distribution costs	370	289
Administration expenses	1,966	1,969
Profit / (loss) from operations	359	(104)
Finance costs	45	110
Profit / (loss) before taxation	314	(214)
Taxation	45	-
Profit / (loss) for the year	269	(214)

James Limited: Statement of Financial Position

	20-2	20-1
	£000	£000
ASSETS		
Non-current assets		
Property, plant and equipment	1,491	1,485
Current assets		
Inventories	370	296
Trade and other receivables	1,202	1,115
Cash	167	-
	1,739	1,411
Total assets	3,230	2,896
EQUITY AND LIABILITIES		
Equity		
Share capital	750	500
Retained earnings	950	700
Total equity	1,700	1,200
Non-current liabilities		
Borrowing	1,050	500
Current liabilities		
Bank overdraft	-	800
Trade and other payables	480	396
Total liabilities	1,530	1,696
Total equity and liabilities	3,230	2,896

The credit analysis team at Lawson Limited has calculated financial indicators from the financial statements provided by James Limited.

These indicators are shown at the top of the next page.

James Limited	20-2	20-1
Gross profit margin %	45.01	45.02
Operating profit margin %	6.00	−2.17
Interest cover	7.98	none
Current ratio	3.62	1.18
Trade payables payment period in days	53.2	54.94
Trade receivables collection period in days	73.27	85.05
Inventory holding period in days	41.01	41.06
Gearing %	38.18	52.00

The Sales Manager of Lawson Limited has reviewed the financial statements provided by James Limited and the financial indicators shown above and has made comments suggesting that credit should not be given to James Limited, because the company is overtrading.

(a)   Write notes to brief a new member of the credit control team explaining the signs of a company overtrading.

(b)   **You are to** write notes analysing the information given about James Limited and recommend whether the increase in credit should be granted.

Use the data available to you in the financial statements and tables of financial indicators to support your comments.

Task 4

The Sales Department has asked for a credit limit of £18,500 to be given to Howard Limited, a potential new customer. The financial information on this and the next page has been supplied by Howard Limited.

Howard Limited: Statement of Profit or Loss

	20-2	20-1
	£000	£000
Sales revenue	1,750	2,100
Cost of sales	1,083	1,242
Gross profit	667	858
Distribution costs	53	59
Administration expenses	779	748
Profit / (loss) from operations	(165)	51
Finance costs	11	8
Profit / (loss) before taxation	(176)	43
Taxation	-	10
Profit / (loss) for the year	(176)	33

Howard Limited: Statement of Financial Position

	20-2	20-1
	£000	*£000*
ASSETS		
Non-current assets		
Property, plant and equipment	771	613
Current assets		
Inventories	116	112
Trade and other receivables	147	268
Cash	5	11
	268	391
Total assets	1,039	1,004
EQUITY AND LIABILITIES		
Equity		
Share capital	400	350
Retained earnings	158	334
Total equity	558	684
Non-current liabilities		
Borrowing	250	150
Current liabilities		
Borrowings	17	-
Trade and other payables	214	170
Total liabilities	481	320
Total equity and liabilities	1,039	1,004

You have been asked to prepare some points to include in an email to the Chief Credit Controller to assist in his decision whether to give credit to Howard Ltd.

Refer to Howard Ltd's financial statements and complete the points detailed below by inserting the appropriate figure or selecting the correct option.

(a) Sales revenue for 20-2 compared to 20-1 has decreased by [   ] %

which means that the company may have

sold fewer units / increased the unit selling price / experienced an increased demand for its products.

(b) The gross profit margin has **increased / decreased**, which means that the company has

increased the selling price / increased the purchase price / left both the selling and purchase price of its products unchanged.

(c) At operational level the company is making a **profit / loss** which

is not a problem as cash not profit pays liabilities / may be a problem depending on the cash flow of the business / is a problem as profits are needed to pay liabilities / is not a problem as gross profit is sufficient to pay liabilities.

(d) The current ratio measures the **short-term solvency / short-term insolvency / long-term solvency** of an organisation. In this case it has **increased / decreased** and is **less than 1 / still greater than 1**, which is **a sign of insolvency / a sign of poor liquidity / a good sign.**

(e) The quick ratio has **risen / fallen** to [   ] which **is / is not** a major concern in terms of liquidity.

(f) The inventory holding period has **increased / decreased**. This may mean that inventory **is slow moving / could run out / levels are too low.**

(g) The trade payables payment period has **increased / decreased** by [   ] days.

This may indicate that the company has **sufficient / insufficient** liquidity and is **likely / unlikely** to pays its liabilities as they fall due.

(h) On the basis of the financial statements that have been provided to us and the key performance indicators I recommend that **credit be given / credit not be given** to Howard Ltd.

Task 5

(a) Efficient day-to-day collection by a business of money owed by customers is best achieved through:

(a) The use of an outside debt collection agency	
(b) A clearly set out and comprehensive credit control policy	
(c) The use of the Small Claims procedure	

Tick **one** option.

A small business has a £7,000 debt outstanding on a customer account. Despite all its efforts, including a solicitor's letter, the business is unable to recover the money. Through which Court process should this claim be pursued?

(a) Multi Track	
(b) Fast Track	
(c) Small Claims Track	

Tick the **one** appropriate option.

A garnishee order is:

(a) A court order sent to a third party such as a bank which has an account for the customer requiring the money to be paid direct to the seller	
(b) An order for the court bailiffs to enter the property of the customer who owes money to the seller to seize valuable assets	
(c) An order which will give the seller a right to the sale proceeds of property owned by the customer	

Tick the **one** correct option.

(b) Select True or False about the following statements relating to retention of title.

	True	False
(a) A seller can reclaim goods from a buyer if the seller has a retention of title clause in the sales documentation and the buyer has paid for the goods in full		
(b) A seller can reclaim goods from a buyer if the seller has a retention of title clause in the sales documentation, the goods are clearly identifiable and the buyer is refusing to pay for the goods		
(c) A seller can reclaim goods from a buyer regardless of whether there is a retention of title clause in the sales documentation, the goods are clearly identifiable and the buyer is refusing to pay for the goods		
(d) A seller can reclaim goods from a buyer if the seller has a retention of title clause in the sales documentation, the goods have been processed and the buyer is refusing to pay for the goods		

(c) Pink Ltd has total receivables ledger balances of £2,500,000, including £50,000 of debts over 90 days old.

Distinct Insurance can provide Pink Ltd with a facility where Distinct Insurance will manage the receivables ledger up to a maximum of £2,000,000, or 80% of the outstanding receivables (excluding debts over 90 days old).

Distinct Insurance is offering:

Recourse factoring	
Non-recourse factoring	
Invoice discounting	
Credit insurance	

The amount Pink Ltd can borrow is: £ _____

(d) Administration as it relates to insolvency can be defined as:

(a) The situation where a company having solvency problems is placed in the hands of an Administrator appointed by the court; the administration process helps to protect the business and will try to return it to solvency	
(b) The situation where a bank that has a floating charge over the assets of a company can appoint an Administrative Receiver who is authorised to sell the secured assets of the company in order to repay the bank borrowing	
(c) The situation where a court makes an order authorising bailiffs to obtain and sell off the assets owned by a business which refuses to pay its trade debts	

Tick the **one** correct option.

(e)   Below is the trade receivables analysis for Davidson Ltd:

Customer	Credit Limit	Balance	0 - 30 days	31 - 60 days	61 - 90 days	Over 90 days
	£	£	£	£	£	£
Graphic Design Ltd	90,000	86,000	86,000			
Cole and Co	20,000	26,000		13,000	13,000	
Stable Ltd	20,000	11,520	11,000			520
Strategy Ltd	28,000	18,500	8,500	7,000	3,000	

From the information given select the correct words to complete the following statements:

[   ] has exceeded its credit limit and the account should be put on stop.

The amounts owed by [   ] represent over 50% of the receivables ledger.

[   ] % of the debts are over 30 days old and the correct credit control procedures should be followed to chase the amounts due.

[   ] appears to pay its debts on time, but there is an old debt which needs further investigation.

Graphic Design Ltd	Cole and Co	Stable Ltd
Strategy Ltd	14	26
61	74	100

(f)   Albert has instructed his builder to carry out an office extension. The builder has left the job with no windows.

The remedy available to Albert is:

(a) Action for breach	
(b) Action for price	
(c) Specific performance	
(d) Action for restitution	

Task 6

(a) **Klunee Ltd**

Klunee Ltd owes a balance of £42,720 including VAT. The account is on stop. Attempts to contact the customer by telephone have been unsuccessful. The account is 80% credit insured.

Complete the sentence below:

Contact the credit insurer to make a claim for £ [   ] , make a provision for

£ [   ] and claim VAT of £ [   ] from HMRC.

(b) Pargetter Ltd's standard credit terms of payment are 30 days. It offers to customers a prompt payment discount of 1.5% for payment within 15 days of invoice.

The simple annual interest rate of the discount is: [   ] per cent.

The compound annual rate of discount is: [   ] per cent.

Calculations should be to two decimal places.

(c) Green Ltd is a regular customer of Geller Ltd. During the year Green Ltd bought from Geller Ltd 650 items which cost £250 each, including VAT at 20%. At the end of the year Green Ltd's balance of account was £13,500.

The receivables collection period (to the nearest day) is: [   ] days.

(d) Below is the expected sales revenue for Evergreen for the next three months:

	Sales revenue
	£
Month 1	40,000
Month 2	35,000
Month 3	42,000

Evergreen predicts that 95% of the sales for month 1 will be paid and 90% of the sales for months 2 and 3 will be paid. The remaining amounts are predicted to be irrecoverable and will be written off.

Calculate the cost to Evergreen for the three months of writing off the irrecoverable amounts:

£ [   ]

(e)   Types of credit insurance include:

1   Whole turnover

2   Key account

3   Single account

4   Catastrophe

Select the correct answer:

(a) 1 and 2 only	
(b) 1, 2 and 3 only	
(c) 2 and 3 only	
(d) 1, 2, 3 and 4	

(f)   Amelia has received a letter from the liquidator of David Ltd. Amelia is owed £4,300 by David Ltd. The letter states that all unsecured creditors of David Ltd will receive a dividend of 3.67p in the pound.

Calculate the amount that Amelia should receive:

£ [   ]

Task 7

Snowden Ltd supplies goods to the manufacturing sector. The standard terms and conditions printed on the back of every sales invoice raised by Snowden Ltd include a retention of title clause and also a requirement that problems with goods must be notified to Snowden Ltd within 24 hours of delivery. Goods returned are subject to a restocking fee of 10%.

You work in the Credit Control Department and the date is 30 September 20-3, the company's financial year-end.

The Senior Credit Controller is ill but has left you a copy of the company's credit control policy together with notes on some of the customer accounts. An extract of these notes is provided below:

Credit control procedures

1. An order for goods is received by email, fax or phone (all phone calls are recorded).

2. Goods are delivered and a goods received note is signed by the customer.

3. The goods received notes are kept in a file in the accounts office.

4. An invoice will be issued on the day after delivery on 30 day terms.

5. An aged analysis of trade receivables is produced weekly.

6. A reminder telephone call is made when the debt is 7 days overdue.

7. When a debt is 14 days overdue a letter is sent.

8. When a debt is 28 days overdue the account will be put on stop.

9. The debt will either be placed in the hands of a debt collection company or legal proceedings could be instigated if the customer does not respond to calls or letters.

10. The business is credit insured, however insurance is only given for customers once they have a history of trade with the business of at least 12 months and have successfully paid for at least three invoiced amounts. Only 70% of the value of the debt is insured.

11. All sales invoices include VAT at the standard rate of 20% and VAT is recovered from HMRC under its Bad Debt Relief Scheme where applicable.

(a)   Review the information provided for each of three customers of Snowden Ltd on the next two pages and prepare a list of actions for collecting the outstanding amounts due to Snowden Ltd.

Your list of actions should include a summary of the options available for the company to pursue and recommendations for provisions or write-off of irrecoverable debts where appropriate.

Downside Ltd

The sales ledger of Snowden Ltd shows a balance outstanding of £67,200 which relates to one invoice dated 31 August 20-3. You have seen in the local papers that Downside Ltd went into administration on 14 September 20-3.

Whistle Ltd

Whistle Ltd has gone into liquidation owing Snowden Ltd £5,400 (including VAT) for a debt which is over six months old. Snowden Ltd has contacted the liquidator who has stated that it is unlikely that the retention of title will be valid because Whistle Ltd purchased similar items from several suppliers and therefore the goods are not identified as being supplied by Snowden Ltd.

Vanilla Ltd

Vanilla Ltd are refusing to pay an invoice of £9,600 from June 20-3 claiming that the goods were not ordered. They are requesting that Snowden Ltd collect the goods. Vanilla Ltd has been a customer for many years and normally pays promptly; all subsequent invoices have been paid in full. There is no record of the order; however, the goods received note was signed by Vanilla Ltd.

You also have to deal with one further customer, Mountain Limited.

(b) **Mountain Ltd**

The sales ledger account for Mountain Ltd has become corrupted but the following information is available:

- Balance 1 August 20-3 = £45,000

- Invoices raised: 2 August 20-3 £10,000 plus VAT at 20%, 24 September 20-3 £3,840 (VAT inclusive)

- Credit notes raised: 6 August 20-3 £1,200 (VAT inclusive) subject to a restocking fee of 10%

- Bank receipts: 16 August 20-3 £45,000, 16 September 20-3 £10,000

You are to calculate the balances on the account of Mountain Ltd at 31 August 20-3 and 30 September 20-3.

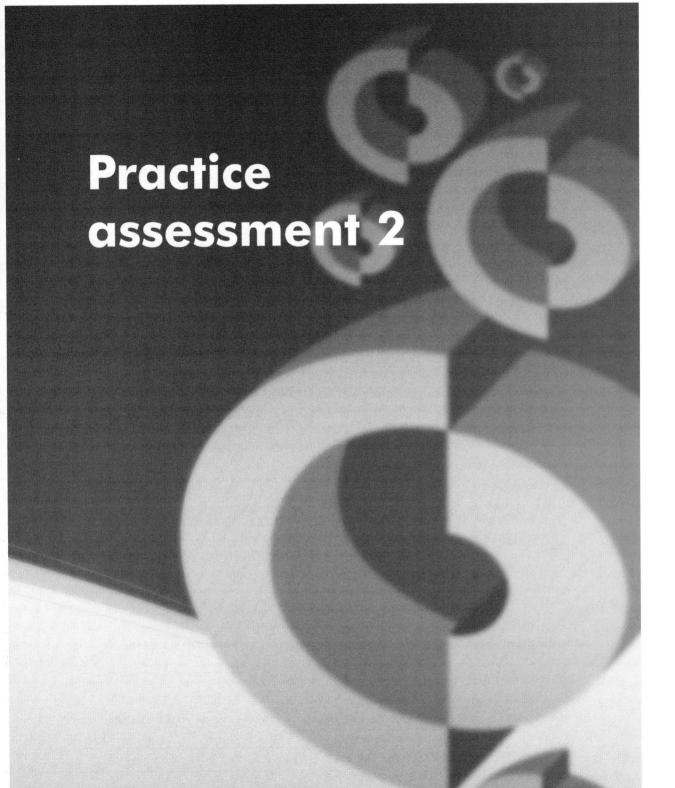

Practice
assessment 2

Task 1

(a) Match the following statements:

	There are conditions in the small print of a contract which the purchaser does not understand
	A contract can be a domestic arrangement between relations
The intention to create legal relations in contract law means	There are conditions in the small print of a contract which a court of law would find unreasonable
	The agreement can be enforced in a court of law if necessary
The Unfair Contract Terms Act gives protection to the purchases of goods and services and means	The contract is part of a fraud or illegal scam
	A contract needs to be approved by a solicitor

(b) A customer owes £6,000 (excluding VAT at 20%). The interest charge under the Late Payments of Commercial Debts (Interest) Act to the nearest penny is £83.83. The bank base rate is 0.5%.

The debt is [   ] days late.

(c) **You are to** enter each of the following phrases into the correct box within the text which follows.

hire purchase agreements   **granting of credit**   **credit sale agreements**

The Consumer Credit Act regulates most agreements for the [   ].

These include [   ] where ownership passes to the

purchaser straightaway on purchase and also [   ]

where the consumer pays instalments to hire the item but will only take ownership when the final

instalment has been paid.

(d) Leroy wants to sell his motor bike for £25,000. He puts a notice in the paper advertising the price but nobody replies. He says to a friend 'You can buy this motor bike at a knock-down price of £20,000. If I don't hear from you within one week I will consider the deal is done.'

In this case his friend has provided:

(a) An acceptance	
(b) No acceptance	
(c) A counter offer	

Tick the **one** correct option.

'Action for the price' means:

(a) Taking legal action in the courts for recovery of an unpaid debt	
(b) Increasing the price of goods beyond the contracted amount	
(c) Effective communication of the price of goods to the buyer	

Tick the **one** correct option.

(e) Select True or False for the following statements:

	True	False
(a) An offer in relation to a contract of sale may be terminated when a time limit fixed for acceptance has expired		
(b) An offer in relation to a contract of sale may be terminated by the buyer making a counter offer		
(c) An offer in relation to a contract of sale may be terminated if the buyer decides to back out of the contract after it has been agreed		
(d) An online bookshop offers for sale a new book "Credit Control in a Nutshell" with the offer of a 20% discount for the first month. This constitutes in contract law consideration.		

Task 2

You work in the finance section of Standard Services Ltd which uses a credit rating system to assess the credit status of new and existing customers. Part of your role is to use the credit rating (scoring) system to assess the risk of default by calculating key indicators (ratios), comparing them to the table and calculating an aggregate score. This system is set out below.

Credit rating (scoring) system	Score
Operating profit margin	
Losses	−5
Less than 5%	0
5% and above but less than 10%	5
10% and above but less than 20%	10
20% or more	20
Interest cover	
No cover	−30
Less than 1	−20
1 and above but less than 2	−10
2 and above but less than 4	0
4 or more	10
Liquidity ratio	
Less than 1	−20
1 and above but less than 1.25	−10
1.25 and above but less than 1.5	0
1.5 or more	10
Gearing (total debt / total debt plus equity)	
Less than 25%	20
25% and above but less than 50%	10
50% and above but less than 65%	0
65% and above but less than 75%	−20
75% and above but less than 80%	−40
80% or more	−100

Risk	Aggregate score
Very low risk	Between 60 and 21
Low risk	Between 20 and 1
Medium risk	Between 0 and –24
High risk	Between –25 and –50
Very high risk	Between –50 and –160

The Sales Department has asked for a credit limit of £16,000 to be given to SKP Limited, a potential new customer. The financial statements on this and the next page have been supplied by SKP Limited.

SKP Limited: Statement of Profit or Loss

	20-2	20-1
	£	£
Sales revenue	1,565,000	1,784,000
Cost of sales	1,181,575	1,202,416
Gross profit	383,425	581,584
Distribution costs	40,784	35,266
Administration expenses	593,041	474,958
Profit / (loss) from operations	(250,400)	71,360
Finance costs	12,520	11,150
Profit / (loss) before taxation	(262,920)	60,210
Taxation	-	12,000
Profit / (loss) for the year	(262,920)	48,210

SKP Limited: Statement of Financial Position

	20-2	20-1
	£	£
ASSETS		
Non-current assets		
Property, plant and equipment	497,755	658,625
Current assets		
Inventories	150,625	73,500
Trade and other receivables	235,000	181,000
Cash	1,450	19,625
	387,075	274,125
Total assets	884,830	932,750
EQUITY AND LIABILITIES		
Equity		
Share capital	100,000	100,000
Retained earnings	37,080	300,000
Total equity	137,080	400,000
Non-current liabilities		
Borrowing	450,000	350,000
Current liabilities		
Trade and other payables	297,750	182,750
Total liabilities	747,750	532,750
Total equity and liabilities	884,830	932,750

(a)   Complete the table below by calculating the key indicators (to two decimal places) for 20-2 and 20-1 for SKP Limited, and rate the company using the credit rating scoring system.

SKP Limited	20-2 Indicator	20-2 Rating	20-1 Indicator	20-1 Rating
Operating profit margin %				
Interest cover				
Current ratio				
Gearing %				
Total credit rating				

(b) Based on the results of your credit rating and using the table below, recommend whether the requested credit limit should be given to SKP Limited.

Rating	Decision
Very low or low risk current year and very low or low risk previous year	Accept
Very low or low risk current year and medium risk previous year	Accept
Very low or low risk current year and high or very high risk previous year	Request latest management accounts and defer decision
Very high risk or high risk current year	Reject
Medium risk current year and medium, low or very low risk previous year	Accept
Medium risk current year and high or very high risk previous year	Request latest management accounts and defer decision

Credit decision	
(a) Accept	
(b) Reject	
(c) Request latest management accounts and defer decision	

Task 3

Lily Limited is a potential new customer of Pascale Direct Limited and has requested a credit limit of £150,000. Lily Limited has supplied the Statement of Profit or Loss below and the Statement of Financial Position on the next page.

Lily Limited: Statement of Profit or Loss

	20-3	20-2
	£000	£000
Sales revenue	10,600	5,900
Cost of sales	7,791	3,894
Gross profit	2,809	2,006
Distribution costs	120	67
Administration expenses	1,414	802
Profit from operations	1,275	1,137
Finance costs	187	18
Profit before taxation	1,088	1,119
Taxation	215	249
Profit for the year	873	870

Lily Limited: Statement of Financial Position

	20-3	20-2
	£000	£000
ASSETS		
Non-current assets		
Property, plant and equipment	1,049	1,105
Current assets		
Inventories	652	650
Trade and other receivables	2,846	947
Cash	-	784
	3,498	2,381
Total assets	4,547	3,486
EQUITY AND LIABILITIES		
Equity		
Share capital	1,300	1,300
Retained earnings	277	938
Total equity	1,577	2,238
Non-current liabilities		
Borrowing	500	800
Current liabilities		
Bank overdraft	698	-
Trade and other payables	1,772	448
Total liabilities	2,970	1,248
Total equity and liabilities	4,547	3,486

The Finance Manager at Pascale Direct Limited has calculated financial indicators from the financial statements provided by Lily Limited.

These indicators are shown at the top of the next page.

Lily Limited	20-3	20-2
Gross profit margin %	26.5	34
Operating profit margin %	12.03	19.27
Interest cover	6.82	63.17
Current ratio	1.42	5.31
Trade payables payment period in days	83.02	41.99
Trade receivables collection period in days	98	58.59
Inventory holding period in days	30.55	60.93
Gearing %	43.17	26.33

A trainee Sales Line Manager of Pascale Direct Limited has reviewed the financial statements provided by Lily Limited and the financial indicators shown above and has made comments suggesting that Lily Limited should be granted an increase in its credit limit. These comments are set out below.

1.   The company turnover has increased by 44.34% from £5.9 million to £10.6 million. This is an excellent sign which shows that the company is expanding.

2.   The gross profit has increased from £2,006,000 to £2,809,000. This means that more cash is available to pay debts.

3.   The profit from operations has increased by £138,000 and the profit after tax has remained the same which is a good sign.

4.   The interest cover is now much better than the previous year, when it was too high.

5.   The current ratio has fallen, but it is still over 1 which means the company is solvent.

6.   The trade receivables have increased by £1,899,000 which is a good sign as it is far less than the increase in turnover of £4,700,000.

7.   The trade payables payment period has increased from 42 days to 83 days; this implies that the company is taking advantage of good credit terms from suppliers.

8.   The inventory has remained the same which is an excellent sign.

9.   Gearing has increased which means that the banks are happy to lend money to this business.

(a)   **You are to** write bullet point notes dealing with the accuracy and validity of each comment that the trainee Sales Line Manager has made. Recommend whether the request for credit should be granted.

Use the data available to you in the financial statements and table of financial indicators to support your comments.

(b)   Write notes for the trainee Sales Line Manager on two other sources of external information which could be used when assessing whether to grant credit to a new customer. Explain the limitations of each source of information.

Task 4

The Sales Department has asked for a credit limit of £34,000 to be given to Weber Limited who is a potential new customer. The financial information below has been supplied by Weber Limited.

Weber Limited: Statement of Profit or Loss

	20-4	20-3
	£000	£000
Sales revenue	3,988	3,560
Cost of sales	1,557	1,424
Gross profit	2,431	2,136
Distribution costs	79	63
Administration expenses	1,485	1,352
Profit from operations	867	721
Finance costs	131	103
Profit before taxation	736	618
Taxation	88	75
Profit for the year	648	543

Weber Limited: Statement of Financial Position

	20-4	20-3
	£000	*£000*
ASSETS		
Non-current assets		
Property, plant and equipment	4,231	3,873
Current assets		
Inventories	151	137
Trade and other receivables	606	585
Cash	101	86
	858	808
Total assets	5,089	4,681
EQUITY AND LIABILITIES		
Equity		
Share capital	2,500	2,500
Retained earnings	491	400
Total equity	2,991	2,900
Non-current liabilities		
Borrowing	1,850	1,550
Current liabilities		
Trade and other payables	248	231
Total liabilities	2,098	1,781
Total equity and liabilities	5,089	4,681

You have been asked to prepare points to include in an email to the Chief Credit Controller to assist in his decision whether to give credit to Weber Ltd.

Refer to Weber Ltd's financial statements and the key performance indicators calculated in (a) and complete the points set out below by inserting the appropriate figure or selecting the correct option.

(a) Sales revenue for 20-4 compared to 20-3 has increased by [   ] %

which means that the company may have

sold fewer units / decreased the unit selling price / experienced an increased demand for its products.

(b) The gross profit margin has remained constant, which indicates that the company has

increased the selling price / increased the purchase price / made no change to the selling and purchase price of its product.

(c) The company is making a **profit / loss** at operational level and the operating profit margin has **increased / decreased**.

(d) The trade payables payment period measures on average the number of days that **inventory is held / customers take to pay / the company takes to pay its suppliers**. For Weber Ltd this has **risen / fallen** slightly.

(e) The current ratio is **less than 1 / greater than 1**, which is a **sign of insolvency / sign of poor liquidity / good sign**.

(f) The quick ratio is **less than 1 / more than 1** which **is / is not** a major concern in terms of liquidity.

(g) The inventory holding period has remained constant. This is a **good sign / bad sign** and indicates **stability / that inventory could run out / that inventory levels are too low**.

(h) Overall it appears that the company is **solvent / insolvent** and has **sufficient / insufficient** liquidity to pays its liabilities as they fall due.

(i) On the basis of the financial statements that have been provided to us and the key performance indicators, I recommend that **credit be given / credit not be given** to Weber Ltd.

Task 5

(a) Match each judgement with the correct definition:

Warrant of execution	A court order sent to a third party such as a bank which has an account for the customer requiring the money to be paid direct to the seller
	An order for the court bailiffs to seize assets belonging to the customer who owes money to the seller
Warrant of delivery	An order which will authorise an employer to deduct regular amounts from the customer's salary in order to repay the debt
	The registration of a charge on a property which belongs to the customer and entitles the seller to be paid once the property is sold
Attachment of earnings	An order for the court bailiffs to seize goods belonging to the seller and held by a customer who owes money to the seller

(b) Select True or False about the following statements if a retention of title claim is to be successfully enforced:

		True	False
(a)	The goods subject to the clause do not need to be clearly identifiable		
(b)	There must be a retention of title clause shown on the sales documentation		
(c)	Goods which have been altered can be repossessed		
(d)	The retention of title clause can only be shown on the sales invoices		

(c) Pink Ltd has total receivables ledger balances of £2,500,000, including £50,000 of debts over 90 days old.

Dashboard Ltd pays £1,000 per month to Alexia Insurance for key account insurance.

During the year Dashboard Ltd had irrecoverable debts of £5,000 which were covered by the insurance.

Alexia Insurance is offering:

Recourse factoring	
Non-recourse factoring	
Invoice discounting	
Credit insurance	

The overall cost to Dashboard Ltd for the year is: £ _____

(d) An Administrative Receiver is an insolvency practitioner who is:

(a)	Appointed by the court in the situation where a company is having solvency problems and the court considers the Administrative Receiver has a reasonable chance of being able to rescue the company	
(b)	Appointed by a bank under its floating charge and is authorised to sell the secured assets of the company in order to repay the bank borrowing in preference to unsecured trade payables	
(c)	Appointed by the court in a company liquidation and has the task of calculating how much goes to each payable when the company assets are sold	

(e) Select the correct words to complete the following statements:

The 80/20 rule states that _____ % of customer accounts make up _____ % of the total value of outstanding debts.

The _____ indicates how long a customer takes to pay debts.

Slow paying customers can be highlighted by using the _____ .

aged receivables analysis	20	credit control policy	
100	average period of credit	80	

(f)   A business has a £2,000 debt outstanding on a customer account. One of the excuses made by the customer for non-payment is that it had not issued a Purchase Order and the seller had consequently sent the wrong goods. Given these circumstances, what is the remedy (if any) that the seller should pursue?

(a)	A County Court action for the amount owed for the goods supplied	
(b)	A Statutory Demand for the amount owed for the goods supplied	
(c)	As there was no defined offer or acceptance there is unlikely to be a contract and so no remedies are likely to succeed	

Tick the appropriate option.

Task 6

(a)   Identify whether each of the statements below is True or False if a claim for VAT bad debt relief is to be made to HMRC.

	True	False
(a) The debt must have remained unpaid for three months after the due date for payment		
(b) The debt must have been written off in the accounts		
(c) The VAT on the debt must have been included on a previous VAT Return		
(d) The debt must be less than four years old		

(b)   Carter Ltd's standard credit terms of payment are 60 days. It offers to customers aprompt payment discount of 2% for payment within 30 days of invoice.

The simple annual interest rate of the discount is: ⬚ per cent.

The compund annual interest rate of the discount is: ⬚ per cent.

Calculations should be to two decimal places.

(c)   Which **one** of the following will improve liquidity?

(a) Adding a retention of title clause to all sales documentation	
(b) Increasing profits by increasing sales	
(c) Ensuring all goods sold are compliant with the Consumer Rights Act	
(d) The introduction of a factoring company to manage trade receivables	

(d)   Daniel has introduced a 3% discount if customers settle invoices in the same month. All sales are on credit. Daniel estimates that 75% of customers will pay in the month of sale and the remainder in the following month. Daniel's expected sales revenue is:

Sales revenue

£

Month 1	78,000
Month 2	80,000

Calculate the expected cash receipts in month 2: £ _____

(e)   Features of recourse factoring include:

1   Replacing cash lost when a debt becomes irrecoverable

2   Taking over the administration of the trade receivables ledger

3   Lending a percentage of the outstanding invoices as soon as they are issued

4   Paying the balance (less charges) of an invoice, once a customer settles the debt

Select the correct answer:

(a) 1, 2 and 3 only	
(b) 2, 3 and 4 only	
(c) 1, 3 and 4 only	
(d) 1, 2, 3 and 4	

(f)   Amelia has received a letter from the liquidator of David Ltd. Amelia is owed £4,300 by David Ltd. The letter states that all unsecured creditors of David Ltd will receive a dividend of 3.67p in the pound.

Calculate the amount that Amelia should receive: £ _____

Task 7

Stable Ltd supplies goods to the manufacturing sector. You work in the Credit Control Department and the date is 31 July 20-3, the company's financial year-end.

The Senior Credit Controller is away on holiday but has left you a copy of the company's credit control policy together with notes on some of the customer accounts.

An extract of these notes is provided below.

Stable Ltd - Notes on credit control procedure

1. An order for goods is received by email, fax or phone (all phone calls are recorded).

2. Goods are delivered and a goods received note is signed by the customer.

3. The goods received notes are kept in a file in the accounts office.

4. An invoice will be issued on the day after delivery on 30 day terms.

5. An aged analysis of trade receivables is produced weekly.

6. A reminder telephone call is made when the debt is 7 days overdue.

7. When a debt is 14 days overdue a letter is sent.

8. When a debt is 28 days overdue the account will be put on stop.

9. The debt will either be placed in the hands of a debt collection company or legal proceedings could be instigated if the customer does not respond to calls or letters.

10. The business is credit insured, however insurance is only given for customers once they have a history of trade with the business of at least 12 months and have successfully paid for at least three invoiced amounts. Only 70% of the value of the debt is insured.

11. All sales invoices include VAT at the standard rate of 20% and VAT is recovered from HMRC under its Bad Debt Relief Scheme where applicable.

(a)   **You are to** review the information provided for each of three customers of Stable Ltd on the next two pages and prepare a list of actions for collecting the outstanding amounts due to Stable Ltd.

Your list of actions should include a summary of the options available for the company to pursue and recommendations for provisions or write-off of irrecoverable debts where appropriate.

Magnum Ltd

The sales ledger of Magnum Ltd shows a balance outstanding of £15,600 which is now 90 days overdue. All letters and telephone calls have been ignored.

Hudsons Inc

Hudsons Inc is an overseas customer with a credit limit of £50,000; they have just placed an order for £35,000 and have an existing balance on the sales ledger of £25,000.

Shoreline Ltd

Shoreline Ltd has a balance outstanding of £33,240, which is made up of an invoice for £29,400 dated 30 June 20-3 and an invoice for £3,840 dated 31 May 20-3. Shoreline Ltd is a regular customer and usually pays on time.

(b) **Sheila Mary Ltd**

The sales ledger account for Sheila Mary Ltd has become corrupted but the following information is available:

- Balance 1 June 20-3 = £165,000

- Invoices raised: 8 June 20-3 £60,000 plus VAT at 20%, 15 July 20-3 £67,200 (VAT inclusive)

- Credit notes raised: 6 June 20-3 £3,000 (VAT inclusive), 17 July 20-3 £5,520 (VAT inclusive)

- Bank receipts: 5 June 20-3 £162,000, 20 July 20-3 £72,000

You are to calculate the balances on the account of Sheila Mary Ltd at 30 June 20-3 and 31 July 20-3.

Practice
assessment 3

Task 1

(a)   Select the correct words to complete the following statements:

An acceptance of an offer must be [   ].

An offer in contract law for the sale of goods may be terminated when [   ].

A person who sues for damages is someone who [   ]

in the courts for [   ].

takes legal action	a counter offer is made	conditional
unconditional	money compensation for breach of contract	seeks legal advice
the goods are found to be faulty	the price is unacceptable	made at the same time as consideration

(b)   A customer owes £7,000 (excluding VAT at 20%) and the debt is 60 days late.

You are to calculate the interest charge under the Late Payments of Commercial Debts (Interest) Act to the nearest penny. Enter the figure in the box below. The bank base rate is 1.5%.

£ [   ]

(c)   Select True or False about the following in relation to the Data Protection Act:

	True	False
(a) The Data Protection Act gives protection for information relating to individuals		
(b) The Data Protection Act gives protection for information relating to limited companies		
(c) Individuals can request that data relating to them will not be used for direct marketing purposes		
(d) Data can only be held for up to one year		

(d) Destiny is a consultancy firm providing IT support to HR Systems. Destiny normally charges £650 per day for IT support. A contract with HR Systems was signed and commenced on 1 January 20-4 for a period of five months with a planned total of 50 days support. The agreed rate was £600 per day subject to a minimum of 40 days support. HR Systems decides how many days will be worked in a month.

A total of 28 days support was provided between 1 January 20-4 and 31 March 20-4. The invoiced amount to date is £16,800. During April and May 20-4 Destiny provided 11 days support.

How much should Destiny invoice HR Systems for April and May 20-4?

(a) £6,600	
(b) £7,150	
(c) £7,200	
(d) £7,800	

(e) Mario offers to buy a signed photograph of the famous actress Scarlett Johansson from a friend. He does not have much money so the friend as a favour lets him have it for £5 when in fact it could sell for over £100. The situation in contract law is that:

(a) The £5 is sufficient consideration even if a very low price is set as a favour to the buyer	
(b) The £5 is not sufficient consideration because the price does not reflect the true value of the photograph	
(c) Mario now owes his friend £95	

Tick the **one** correct option.

Otto tells his daughter Cordelia that he is leaving her £5,000 in his will. The next day Otto falls off a ladder and is tragically killed. Cordelia then spends £3,000 on computer equipment for the business she runs, relying on the fact that the £5,000 will be coming to her. It turns out that the amount left in the will to Cordelia was actually only £500. Cordelia wants to know what her legal position is and if there is a contract. The correct advice would be:

(a) There is no valid contract because the agreement was a domestic one and not intended to create legal relations	
(b) There is no valid contract because Otto has died	
(c) There is a valid contract and Cordelia is entitled to put in a claim to the solicitors dealing with Otto's will	

Tick the **one** correct option.

Task 2

You work as a Credit Control Manager for Purple Planet Ltd which uses a credit rating system to assess the credit status of new customers. The credit rating (scoring) system is used to assess the risk of default by calculating key indicators (ratios), comparing them to the table and calculating an aggregate score. This system is set out below.

Credit rating (scoring) system	Score
Operating profit margin	
Losses	−5
Less than 5%	0
5% and above but less than 10%	5
10% and above but less than 20%	10
20% or more	20
Interest cover	
No cover	−30
Less than 1	−20
1 and above but less than 2	−10
2 and above but less than 4	0
4 or more	10
Liquidity ratio	
Less than 1	−20
1 and above but less than 1.25	−10
1.25 and above but less than 1.5	0
1.5 or more	10
Gearing (total debt / total debt plus equity)	
Less than 25%	20
25% and above but less than 50%	10
50% and above but less than 65%	0
65% and above but less than 75%	−20
75% and above but less than 80%	−40
80% or more	−100

Risk	Aggregate score
Very low risk	Between 60 and 21
Low risk	Between 20 and 1
Medium risk	Between 0 and −24
High risk	Between −25 and −50
Very high risk	Between −50 and −160

The Sales Department has asked for a credit limit of £55,000 to be given to Garden Design Limited, a new customer.

The financial statements that follow have been supplied by Garden Design Limited.

Garden Design Limited: Statement of Profit or Loss

	20-2	20-1
	£000	£000
Sales revenue	7,500	6,300
Cost of sales	3,639	3,654
Gross profit	3,861	2,646
Distribution costs	758	687
Administration expenses	1,978	2,211
Profit / (loss) from operations	1,125	(252)
Finance costs	35	45
Profit / (loss) before taxation	1,090	(297)
Taxation	220	-
Profit / (loss) for the year	870	(297)

Garden Design Limited: Statement of Financial Position

	20-2	20-1
	£000	£000
ASSETS		
Non-current assets		
Property, plant and equipment	2,004	1,231
Current assets		
Inventories	151	148
Trade and other receivables	1,221	998
Cash	55	486
	1,427	1,632
Total assets	3,431	2,863
EQUITY AND LIABILITIES		
Equity		
Share capital	1,500	800
Retained earnings	360	35
Total equity	1,860	835
Non-current liabilities		
Borrowing	1,000	1,600
Current liabilities		
Trade and other payables	571	428
Total liabilities	1,571	2,028
Total equity and liabilities	3,431	2,863

(a) Complete the table below by calculating the key indicators (to two decimal places) for 20-2 and 20-1 for Garden Design Limited, and assess the company using the credit rating scoring system.

Garden Design Limited	20-2 Indicator	20-2 Rating	20-1 Indicator	20-1 Rating
Operating profit margin %				
Interest cover				
Quick ratio				
Gearing %				
Total credit rating				

(b) Based on the results of your credit rating and using the table below, recommend whether the requested credit limit should be given to Garden Design Limited.

Rating	Decision
Very low or low risk current year and very low or low risk previous year	Accept
Very low or low risk current year and medium risk previous year	Accept
Very low or low risk current year and high or very high risk previous year	Request latest management accounts and defer decision
Very high risk or high risk current year	Reject
Medium risk current year and medium, low or very low risk previous year	Accept
Medium risk current year and high or very high risk previous year	Request latest management accounts and defer decision

Credit decision	
(a) Accept	
(b) Reject	
(c) Request latest management accounts and defer decision	

Task 3

Berry Limited has been trading with Hollywood Limited for several years and has usually kept within its limit. Recently, however, the company has needed chasing for payment of its invoices.

The company has now contacted Hollywood Limited to request an increase in its credit limit from £50,000 to £200,000.

Berry Limited has supplied the financial statements that follow but the figures for 20-3 have not yet been sent to Hollywood Limited, despite several requests. The 20-2 figures are over 18 months old.

Berry Limited: Statement of Profit or Loss

	20-2	20-1
	£000	£000
Sales revenue	5,170	4,575
Cost of sales	2,068	1,830
Gross profit	3,102	2,745
Distribution costs	620	549
Administration expenses	2,747	1,693
Profit / (loss) from operations	(265)	503
Finance costs	-	10
Profit / (loss) before taxation	(265)	493
Taxation	-	81
Profit / (loss) for the year	(265)	412

Berry Limited: Statement of Financial Position

	20-2	20-1
	£000	£000
ASSETS		
Non-current assets		
Property, plant and equipment	2,984	1,056
Current assets		
Inventories	283	266
Trade and other receivables	708	626
Cash	252	186
	1,243	1,078
Total assets	4,227	2,134
EQUITY AND LIABILITIES		
Equity		
Share capital	3,800	1,200
Retained earnings	195	488
Total equity	3,995	1,688
Non-current liabilities		
Borrowing	-	200
Trade and other payables	232	246
Total liabilities	232	446
Total equity and liabilities	4,227	2,134

The credit analysis team at Hollywood Limited has calculated financial indicators from the financial statements provided by Berry Limited.

These indicators are shown at the top of the next page.

Berry Limited	20-2	20-1
Gross profit margin %	60	60
Operating profit margin %	–5.13	10.99
Interest cover	No cover	50.3
Current ratio	5.36	4.38
Trade payables payment period in days	40.95	49.07
Trade receivables collection period in days	49.98	49.94
Inventory holding period in days	49.95	53.05
Gearing %	N/A	10.59

In 20-2 Berry Limited invested £2,500,000 in non-current assets to fund new contracts and these new contracts increased turnover in the later part of the financial year.

The existing non-current assets were rendered obsolete and the book value was written off to administration expenses in 20-2.

The Sales Manager of Hollywood Limited has stated that he has been reliably informed by the Finance Director of Berry Limited (his brother in law) that the turnover of Berry Limited has increased significantly. He therefore requests that the credit limit increase should be sanctioned immediately without having to go through the usual checks.

(a)   **You are to** write notes analysing the information given about Berry Limited and recommend whether the increase in credit should be granted.

Use the data available to you in the financial statements and tables of financial indicators to support your comments.

(b)   Write notes on objectivity and credit control, taking the comments made by the Sales Manager into account.

Task 4

The Sales Department has asked for a credit limit of £18,000 to be given to Joseph Limited who is a potential new customer.

The financial statements that follow have been supplied by Joseph Limited.

Joseph Limited: Statement of Profit or Loss

	20-3	20-2
	£000	£000
Sales revenue	6,124	4,536
Cost of sales	4,284	3,183
Gross profit	1,840	1,353
Distribution costs	306	181
Administration expenses	919	723
Profit from operations	615	449
Finance costs	38	10
Profit before taxation	577	439
Taxation	120	90
Profit for the year	457	349

Joseph Limited: Statement of Financial Position

	20-3	20-2
	£000	*£000*
ASSETS		
Non-current assets		
Property, plant and equipment	2,520	1,381
Current assets		
Inventories	328	392
Trade and other receivables	684	435
Cash	-	27
	1,012	854
Total assets	3,532	2,235
EQUITY AND LIABILITIES		
Equity		
Share capital	1,250	1,000
Retained earnings	308	496
Total equity	1,558	1,496
Non-current liabilities		
Borrowing	850	250
Current liabilities		
Borrowings	56	-
Trade and other payables	1,068	489
Total liabilities	1,974	739
Total equity and liabilities	3,532	2,235

You have been asked to prepare points to include in an email to the Chief Credit Controller to assist in his decision whether to give credit to Joseph Limited.

Refer to Joseph Limited's financial statements and complete the points set out below by inserting the appropriate figure or selecting the correct option.

(a)   Sales revenue for 20-3 compared to 20-2 has increased by ⬚ %

which means that the company may have

sold fewer units / decreased the unit selling price / either sold more units or increased the selling price of its product.

(b)   Gross profit has increased by ⬚ % and profit from operations has

increased by ⬚ %.

Both the gross profit margin and the operating profit margin have **increased / decreased** slightly.

(c)   The current ratio provides a rough measure of the **long-term solvency / short-term solvency / insolvency** of the organisation.

In the case of Joseph Limited it has **risen / fallen** and is now **less than 1 / greater than 1**, which is a **sign of insolvency / sign of poor liquidity / good sign**.

(d)   The inventory level has **increased / decreased**; this is a **good sign / bad sign** as the inventory holding period has **increased / decreased**, which may mean that **inventory could run out / inventory levels are too high**.

(e)   The quick ratio has **fallen / risen** which **is / is not** a major concern and indicates **poor / good** liquidity.

(f)   The trade payables payment period has **increased / decreased** by ⬚ days.

It appears that the company is **able / finding it more difficult** to pay its liabilities as they fall due.

(g)   On the basis of the financial statements that have been provided to us and the key performance indicators I recommend that **credit be given / credit not be given** to Joseph Limited.

Task 5

(a) Match each statement with the correct court procedure:

A business has a £20,000 debt outstanding on a customer account. The situation is very simple and the case will be concluded within one day.	County Court under the Fast Track
	County Court under the Small Claims Track
£3,000 is owed by a customer. The situation is very simple and the case will be concluded within one day.	High Court under the Fast Track
	Magistrates Court under the Small Claims Track
A business has a £20,000 debt outstanding on a customer account. It is a complex case that will take more than one day to resolve.	County Court under the Multi Track

(b) Donald has a customer who is a sole trader. The customer is refusing to pay. Select True or False for the options Donald thinks are available:

	True	False
(a) There is a retention of title clause, therefore the goods can be reclaimed as they are clearly identifiable		
(b) The debt is three months old; a claim can be made to HMRC to reclaim the VAT		
(c) The debt is credit insured; a claim can be made to recover part of the debt		
(d) The debt is for £1,400; therefore the customer can be issued with a statutory demand for bankruptcy		

(c) Maiden Ltd is considering alternative ways of managing debt collection. The total receivables ledger balances are £1,256,000, which includes two invoices for £503,000 and £217,000.

Trade Finance will lend Maiden Ltd up to 80% against invoices over £300,000.

Trade Finance is offering:

Recourse factoring	
Non-recourse factoring	
Invoice discounting	
Credit insurance	

Maiden Ltd can borrow: £ [   ]

(d) Buffay Ltd is a regular customer of Hartmann Ltd. Amanda, the Credit Controller of Hartmann Ltd, is married to the Financial Director of Buffay Ltd. Amanda regularly fails to contact Buffay Ltd to chase outstanding debts.

This is an example of:

(a)	Lack of due care	
(b)	A conflict of interest	
(c)	Breach of confidentiality	

(e)   Below is the trade receivables analysis of Austen Ltd at 31 October 20-3; invoices are issued on 30 day terms:

Customer	Balance	0 - 30 days	31 - 60 days	61 - 90 days	Over 90 days
	£	£	£	£	£
Clarke Ltd	72,000		72,000		
Day Ltd	17,400				17,400
Horwood Ltd	180,000	60,000	60,000	60,000	
Rhodes Ltd	(678)				(678)
Stein Ltd	115,200	115,200			

From the information given select the correct customer to complete the following statements:

[   ] has one invoice dated 14 September 20-3, a final reminder is being sent to the customer.

The balance for [   ] relates to a credit note for a prompt payment discount created by Austen Ltd in error.

The account for [   ] is not overdue and no action needs to be taken at present.

[   ] has gone into administration; VAT will be reclaimed from HMRC as the correct conditions have been met.

Clarke Ltd	Day Ltd	Horwood Ltd
Rhodes Ltd	Stein Ltd	

(f)   A statutory demand made on a trade receivable for an outstanding debt for a sole trader should be for a minimum of:

(a)	£5,000	
(b)	£1,000	
(c)	£750	

Tick the **one** correct option.

Task 6

(a) **Grimshaw Ltd**

Grimshaw Ltd owes a balance of £18,000 including VAT. The account is on stop. Attempts to contact the customer by telephone have been unsuccessful. The account is not credit insured.

Complete the sentence below:

Contact the credit insurer to make a claim for £ [   ] , make a provision for

£ [   ] and claim VAT of £ [   ] from HMRC.

(b) Aldridge Ltd's standard credit terms of payment are 30 days. It offers to customers a prompt payment discount of 2.5% for payment within 7 days of invoice.

The simple annual interest rate of the discount is: [   ] per cent.

The compund annual interest rate of the discount is: [   ] per cent.

Calculations should be to two decimal places.

(c) You are a trade supplier owed money by Dufco Ltd, which has recently been put into administration. This company owes a great deal of money to the bank. In this case you should:

(a)	Get paid after the bank gets its money back	
(b)	Make a statutory claim to get your money back	
(c)	Try to recover the money and hope that the company recovers	

Tick the **one** appropriate option.

(d)   Helen's customers currently pay 30 days after the month-end. She is introducing a 2% discount from month 2 if customers settle the invoice in the same month. She predicts that 85% of customers will take advantage of this. Expected sales revenue is:

	Sales revenue
	£
Month 1	140,000
Month 2	146,000
Month 3	154,000

Calculate the cost of introducing the discount: £ [   ]

(e)   Which **one** of the following is not a type of credit insurance?

(a) Catastrophe	
(b) Non-recourse factoring	
(c) Single account	
(d) Key account	

(f)   Brunning Ltd is a regular customer of Butcher Ltd. During the year Brunning Ltd bought from Butcher Ltd 23,010 items which cost £44 each, including VAT at 20%. At the end of the year Brunning Ltd's balance of account was £112,500.

The receivables collection period (to the nearest day) is: [   ] days.

Task 7

Opto Ltd supplies goods to the manufacturing sector. Each product is stamped with a batch number so that they can be easily identified. The standard terms and conditions printed on the back of every sales invoice raised by Opto Ltd include a retention of title clause. There is also a clause that states that problems with goods must be notified to Opto Ltd within 24 hours of delivery. Goods returned are subject to a restocking fee of 10%.

You work in the Credit Control Department and the date is 30 June 20-3, the company's financial year-end.

The Senior Credit Controller is away on holiday in Italy but has left you a copy of the company's credit control policy together with notes on how to deal with the customer accounts. The notes are as follows:

Credit control policy summary notes

1.   An order for goods is received by email, fax or phone (all phone calls are recorded).

2.   Goods are delivered and a goods received note is signed by the customer.

3.   The goods received notes are kept in a file in the accounts office.

4.   An invoice will be issued on the day after delivery on 30 day terms.

5.   An aged analysis of trade receivables is produced weekly.

6.   A reminder telephone call is made when the debt is 7 days overdue.

7.   When a debt is 14 days overdue a letter is sent.

8.   When a debt is 28 days overdue the account will be put on stop.

9.   The debt will either be placed in the hands of a debt collection company or legal proceedings could be instigated if the customer does not respond to calls or letters.

10. The business is credit insured, however insurance is only given for customers once they have a history of trade with the business of at least 12 months and have successfully paid for at least three invoiced amounts. Only 70% of the value of the debt is insured.

11. All sales invoices include VAT at the standard rate of 20% and VAT is recovered from HMRC under its Bad Debt Relief Scheme where applicable.

You are to:

(a)   Review the information provided for each of the three customers below and prepare an action plan for each customer for collecting the outstanding amounts due to Opto Ltd.

Your action plan should include a summary of the options available for the company to pursue and recommendations for provisions or write-off of irrecoverable debts where appropriate.

Beck Ltd

Beck Ltd has an amount owing of £3,000 and the debt is over 90 days old. There is no dispute with the order; Beck Ltd is simply refusing to pay.

Free Ltd

Free Ltd has gone into receivership owing Opto Ltd £15,000 (including VAT). Free Ltd has contacted the receiver who has stated that it is unlikely that the retention of title will be valid because the company purchased similar items from several suppliers and therefore the goods are not identified as being supplied by Opto Ltd.

The receiver also stated that the existing debt will be classed as an unsecured creditor by Free Ltd.

Hardy Ltd

Hardy Ltd is a new customer and no credit limit has been allowed. Hardy Ltd paid for goods by cheque when the order was made. The order was processed before the cheque had cleared and the cheque has subsequently bounced. The phone line to Hardy Ltd now appears to have been disconnected.

(b)   Monte Ltd

The sales ledger account held for Monte Ltd is not up-to-date because of a flood in the accounts office. The following information has been gathered together:

Balance of Monte Ltd Account on 1 May 20-3:   £105,000

Invoices raised: 8 May 20-3 £40,000 plus VAT at 20%, 16 June 20-3 £78,000 (VAT inclusive)

Credit notes raised: 10 May 20-3 £18,000 (VAT inclusive) subject to a restocking fee of 10%, 26 June 20-3 £4,800 (VAT inclusive) not subject to a restocking fee

Bank receipts: 10 May 20-3 £100,000, 10 June 20-3 £30,000

What is the balance on the account of Monte Ltd at 31 May 20-3 and 30 June 20-3?

Answers to practice assessment 1

Task 1

(a) An offer in relation to a contract sale can be made **by the buyer or seller**.

A valid contract must contain these four elements: **offer**; **acceptance**; **consideration**; **intention to create legal relations.**

A shop has set up a notice board where customers can advertise goods or services for sale to the public. These adverts constitute in contract law an **invitation to treat.**

(b) £62.88 *Workings: (£5,000 x 1.2) x (0.5% + 8%) x 45/365*

(c) The Data Protection Act protects data held about **individuals** and not **companies**. It covers both computer-based and **manual** records. It is based around eight guiding **principles** which protect the data held.

(d) (c) An offer

(c) The terms of the contract are not fulfilled

(e) (a) and (c) are True; (b) and (d) are False

Task 2

(a)

Sunny Limited	20-3 Indicator	20-3 Rating	20-2 Indicator	20-2 Rating
Operating profit margin %	15	10	20	20
Interest cover	17.5	10	10	10
Quick ratio	1.6	10	1.4	0
Gearing %	41.62	10	51.75	0
Total credit rating		40		30

Workings:

	Formula	**20-3**	**20-2**
Operating profit margin %	Profit from operations x 100 / Sales revenue	630 x 100 / 4,200 = 15%	770 x 100 / 3,850 = 20%
Interest cover	Profit from operations / Interest payable	630 / 36 = 17.5	770 / 77 = 10
Quick ratio	Current assets less inventories / Current liabilities	1,868 – 68 / 380 + 745 = 1.6	2,154 – 54 / 505 + 995 = 1.4
Gearing %	Total debt x 100 / Total debt plus equity	1,230* x 100 / 1,230 + 1,725 = 41.62% *850 + 380	1,555** x 100 / 1,555 + 1,450 = 51.75% **1,050+505

(b)   (a)   Accept

Task 3

(a)   Overtrading occurs when a business expands too rapidly and has insufficient working capital and cash available to support the increased level of trading.

The signs of overtrading are:

- A significant increase in turnover.

- A reduction in the level of credit control, for example extended credit terms, and / or an increase in the trade receivables collection period.

- An increase in irrecoverable debts.

- Reductions in cash balances and / or the introduction or increase in bank overdrafts.

- Failure to pay suppliers on time, which is indicated by an increase in the trade payables payment period, or that payment period being higher than the industry average.

- Falling profit margins.

- A significant increase in the inventory holding period.

- Failure to inject capital, for example equity or long-term loans, to facilitate the increase in turnover.

(b)   **Profitability**

The turnover has increased by £1,203,000 or 25.14% from £4,785,000 to £5,988,000. This may initially indicate a sign of overtrading but other factors must be considered.

Gross profit has increased by £541,000 or 25.12%, which is almost identical to the increase in turnover. The gross profit margin has remained constant at 45%.

Profit from operations has increased by £463,000 and the operating profit margin has increased by 8.17%. This may indicate that the company has not chased turnover at the expense of profits.

Even though there has been a significant increase in turnover, the administration expenses have remained roughly the same, which has meant that the profit for the year has increased significantly.

There is an improvement in interest cover which shows that the finance costs are covered by the profit from operations almost eight times. In the previous year there was no cover.

Liquidity

When assessing the credit worthiness of a business, the higher the current ratio, the better, it is a crude measure of solvency. In this case it has more than doubled from 1.18 in the previous year to 3.62.

The components that make up the current ratio need to be looked at to determine liquidity.

The cash balance of £167,000 has increased by £967,000 from the overdraft of £800,000 in the previous year; this is a strong indicator of improved liquidity.

The trade receivables have increased by 7.8%; this does not indicate overtrading as turnover has increased by 25.14%. The trade receivables collection period has fallen from 85.05 days in the previous year to 73.27, a fall of almost 12 days. This also indicates that the company is not overtrading and suggests there has been an improvement in credit control procedures.

Trade payables have increased by £84,000. This is not unusual given that the cost of sales has increased by a similar proportion. The gross profit margin has remained constant which would suggest that suppliers have not increased their prices. The trade payables payment period has fallen slightly, but it is still significantly lower than the trade receivables collection period.

The increase in inventory has meant that a further £74,000 of working capital has been required. Sales revenue has increased significantly and an increase in inventory would therefore be expected. The inventory holding period has remained constant at 41 days which is a positive sign.

Gearing

Gearing has decreased from 52% in the previous year to 38.18%. The profile of debt has improved by converting a short-term overdraft of £800,000 to a long-term loan of £550,000 and an injection of equity from shareholders of £250,000. This has aided liquidity, but may defer potential cash flow problems to future years.

Recommendation

The increase in credit limit should be granted based on the performance indicators and financial information.

There are no signs that the company is overtrading.

Task 4

(a)   Sales revenue for 20-2 compared to 20-1 has decreased by **16.67%**, which means that the company may have **sold fewer units.**

(b)   The gross profit margin has **decreased**, which means that the company has **increased the purchase price.**

(c)   At operational level the company is making a **loss** which **may be a problem depending on the cash flow of the business.**

(d)   The current ratio measures the **short-term solvency** of an organisation. In this case it has **decreased** and is **still greater than 1**, which is **a good sign**.

(e)   The quick ratio has **fallen** to 0.66 which **is** a major concern in terms of liquidity.

(f)   The inventory holding period has **increased**. This may mean that inventory **is slow moving.**

(g)   The trade payables payment period has **increased** by **22.16** days. This may indicate that the company has **insufficient** liquidity and is **unlikely** to pays its liabilities as they fall due.

(h)   On the basis of the financial statements that have been provided to us and the key performance indicators I recommend that **credit not be given** to Howard Ltd.

Workings:

(a)   Decrease in revenue: (1,750 − 2,100) / 2,100 = −16.67%

(g)   Increase in trade payables payment period: 72.12 − 49.96 = 22.16 days

	Formula	20-2	20-1
Gross profit margin %	$\dfrac{\text{Gross profit} \times 100}{\text{Sales revenue}}$	$\dfrac{667 \times 100}{1,750}$ = 38.11%	$\dfrac{858 \times 100}{2,100}$ = 40.86%
Trade payables pmt period in days	$\dfrac{\text{Trade payables} \times 365}{\text{Cost of sales}}$	$\dfrac{214 \times 365}{1,083}$ = 72.12	$\dfrac{170 \times 365}{1,242}$ = 49.96
Inventory holding period in days	$\dfrac{\text{Inventories} \times 365}{\text{Cost of sales}}$	$\dfrac{116 \times 365}{1,083}$ = 39.1	$\dfrac{112 \times 365}{1,242}$ = 32.91
Current ratio	$\dfrac{\text{Current assets}}{\text{Current liabilities}}$	$\dfrac{268}{17 + 214}$ = 1.16	$\dfrac{391}{170}$ = 2.3
Quick ratio	$\dfrac{\text{Current assets less inventories}}{\text{Current liabilities}}$	$\dfrac{268 - 116}{17 + 214}$ = 0.66	$\dfrac{391 - 112}{170}$ = 1.64

Task 5

(a)   (b)   A clearly set out and comprehensive credit control policy

         (c)   Small Claims Track

         (a)   A court order sent to a third party such as a bank which has an account for the customer requiring the money to be paid direct to the seller

(b)   (b) is True; the remaining statements are False

(c)   Recourse factoring

       £1,960,000

       Workings: (£2,500,000 – £50,000) x 80%

(d)   (a)   The situation where a company having solvency problems is placed in the hands of an Administrator appointed by the court; the administration process helps to protect the business and will try to return it to solvency

(e)   **Cole and Co** has exceeded its credit limit and the account should be put on stop.

       The amounts owed by **Graphic Design Ltd** represent over 50% of the receivables ledger.

       26% of the debts are over 30 days old and the correct credit control procedures should be followed to chase the amounts due.

       Stable Ltd appears to pay its debts on time, but there is an old debt which needs further investigation.

(f)   (c)   Specific performance

Task 6

(a)   Klunee Ltd

Contact the credit insurer to make a claim for **£28,480**, make a provision for **£7,120** and claim VAT of **£7,120** from HMRC.

(b)   The simple annual interest rate of the discount is 37.06%.

Workings:

$$\left(\frac{1.5}{98.5} \right) \quad \times \quad \left(\frac{365}{30-15} \right) \times 100 = 37.06\%$$

The compound annual rate of discount is 44.45%.

Workings:

$$\left\{ \left(1 + \frac{1.5}{98.5} \right)^{\wedge \left(\frac{365}{30-15} \right)} -1 \right\} \times 100 = 44.45\%$$

(c)   The receivables collection period (to the nearest day) is **30** days.

Workings: (£13,500 / [650 x £250]) x 365

(d)   £9,700

Workings: (£40,000 x 5%) + (£35,000 x 10%) + (£42,000 x 10%)

(e)   (d)   1, 2, 3 and 4

(f)   £157.81

Task 7

(a)   Downside Ltd

- The invoice is not overdue, however the fact that the company is now in administration is a worrying sign and the account should be put on stop.
- A reminder telephone call should be made on 7 October 20-3 and an overdue letter sent on 14 October 20-3 if no payment is made.
- Contact the administrator of Downside Ltd and establish the likelihood of the account being paid.
- It will not be possible to instigate legal proceedings whilst the company is in administration.
- If the debt remains unpaid at the end of November 20-3 make a provision in the accounts.

Whistle Ltd

- The liquidator should be contacted and Snowden Ltd must insist that they should be able to visit the premises of Whistle Ltd to attempt to identify the goods supplied by Snowden Ltd.
- The threat of legal action can be made if the liquidator does not allow the visit.
- The VAT of £900 should be reclaimed from HMRC.
- The credit insurer should be contacted and a claim made for £3,150.
- An allowance for an irrecoverable debt of £1,350 should be made in the accounts.

Vanilla Ltd

- There is no evidence of the order, however there is evidence of the delivery and the goods were accepted by Vanilla Ltd, so somewhere a mix up has been made.
- In order to maintain a good relationship with Vanilla Ltd the goods should be picked up from Vanilla Ltd and no charge made.
- A credit note should be raised against the invoice.

(b)   **Mountain Ltd**

Balance at 31 August 20-3 = £10,920

Balance at 30 September 20-3 = £4,760

Note that the question asks for a calculation of the balances of the account at the end of the two months. This may either be carried out as a straight arithmetic exercise, or it can be done by completing two 'T' accounts as shown below.

Dr			**Mountain Limited**			Cr
		£				£
1 Aug	B/d	45,000				
2 Aug	Invoice	12,000	6 Aug	Credit Note		1,080
			16 Aug	Bank		45,000
			31 Aug	C/d		10,920
		57,000				57,000

Dr			**Mountain Limited**			Cr
		£				£
1 Sept	B/d	10,920	16 Sept	Bank		10,000
24 Sept	Invoice	3,840				
			30 Sept	C/d		4,760
		14,760				14,760

Answers to practice assessment 2

Task 1

(a)

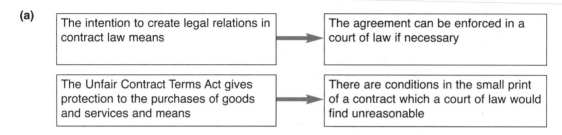

The intention to create legal relations in contract law means	The agreement can be enforced in a court of law if necessary
The Unfair Contract Terms Act gives protection to the purchases of goods and services and means	There are conditions in the small print of a contract which a court of law would find unreasonable

(b) The debt is **50** days late. *Workings:* (£83.83 x 365 ÷ (£6,000 x 1.2) ÷ (0.5% + 8%))

(c) The Consumer Credit Act regulates most agreements for the **granting of credit**. These include **credit sale agreements** where ownership passes to the purchaser straightaway on purchase and also **hire purchase agreements** where the consumer pays instalments to hire the item but will only take ownership when the final instalment has been paid.

(d) (b) No acceptance

(a) Taking legal action in the courts for recovery of an unpaid debt

(e) (a) and (b) are True; (c) and (d) are False

Task 2

(a)

SKP Limited	20-2 Indicator	20-2 Rating	20-1 Indicator	20-1 Rating
Operating profit margin %	−16	−5	4	0
Interest cover	No cover	−30	6.4	10
Current ratio	1.3	0	1.5	10
Gearing %	76.65	−40	46.67	10
Total credit rating		−75		30

Workings:

	Formula	20-2	20-1
Operating profit margin %	Profit from operations x 100 / Sales revenue	(250,400) x100 = −16% / 1,565,000	71,360 x 100 = 4% / 1,784,000
Interest cover	Profit from operations / Interest payable	No cover	71,360 = 6.4 / 11,150
Current ratio	Current assets / Current liabilities	387,075 = 1.3 / 297,750	274,125 = 1.5 / 182,750
Gearing %	Total debt x 100 / Total debt plus equity	450,000 x 100 = 76.65% / 450,000 + 137,080	350,000 x 100 = 46.67% / 350,000 + 400,000

(b)   (b)   Reject

Task 3

(a)   **The company turnover has increased by 44.34% from £5.9 million to £10.6 million. This is an excellent sign which shows that the company is expanding.**

- You are correct that the turnover has increased, but the increase is 79.66% (£4,700,000 / £5,900,000), not 44.34%.

- The fact that turnover has increased significantly may be a sign of overtrading, but other indicators have to be considered.

- These include significant increases in turnover linked to reduced margins, increased levels of current assets and trade cycle days and cash reduction in flow.

- These points will be considered below.

The gross profit has increased from £2,006,000 to £2,809,000. This means that more cash is available to pay debts.

- You are correct that the gross profit has increased by £803,000; however, the gross profit margin has fallen by 7.5% from 34% to 26.5%, which would indicate that suppliers may have increased their prices.

- An increase in gross profit does not mean that more cash is available to pay debts; it depends on where the profit has gone in the period.

- Has it been "invested" or is it "tied up" in inventory, trade receivables or non-current assets?

- This is why it is necessary to consider the liquidity of the business and changes in the assets and liabilities to confirm the liquidity of the business.

The profit from operations has increased by £138,000 and the profit after tax has remained the same which is a good sign.

- The profit from operations has increased, but as with the gross profit margin the operating profit margin has also fallen from 19.27% to 12.03%, a fall of just over 7%.

- This would indicate that the administration and distribution expenses have risen at roughly the same rate as turnover.

- Profit after tax has remained roughly the same due to a significant increase in finance costs.

The interest cover is now much better than the previous year, when it was too high.

- Interest cover has fallen from 63 times in the previous year to just below 7 times.

- Interest cover is a key indicator that is often used by credit agencies and financial institutions to calculate how many times the profit from operations can cover the interest payments.

- The calculation of 6.82 times indicates that the interest paid is covered by the profit from operations by almost 7 times.

- The big reduction in interest cover is due to the company now having a large overdraft which it did not have in the previous year.

- Cash generation is needed to pay interest. Many profitable companies fail because they cannot generate cash to pay their liabilities as they fall due.

The current ratio has fallen, but it is still over 1 which means the company is solvent.

- Referring to the fact that the current ratio is over 1 and therefore the company is solvent is a common misunderstanding; an unacceptable current ratio very much depends on the organisation itself and the type of industry to which it belongs.

- A higher current ratio indicates a better credit worthiness when assessing a potential credit customer.

- The current ratio is a crude measure of solvency and in this case it has decreased significantly from 5.31 in the previous year to 1.42, which may indicate insolvency.

- The components that make up current assets need to be looked at to determine liquidity.

- The cash balance has fallen by £1,482,000 and the company now places a heavy reliance on a short-term overdraft which could be an increased risk to the business.

The trade receivables have increased by £1,899,000 which is a good sign as it is far less than the increase in turnover of £4,700,000.

- Trade receivables have increased from £947,000 to £2,846,000; an increase would be expected with the significant increase in sales revenue.

- However, the collection period has increased by almost 40 days. This would indicate that the company's Credit Control Department is struggling to collect debts and may also point to overtrading.

The trade payables payment period has increased from 42 days to 83 days; this implies that the company is taking advantage of good credit terms from suppliers.

- The trade payables have increased by £1,324,000; an increase would be expected as there has been a significant increase in cost of sales.

- The increase in the trade payables payment period from 42 to 83 days is not a good sign. It indicates that the company is struggling to pay suppliers on time and is another strong indicator of overtrading.

The inventory has remained the same which is an excellent sign.

- Inventory levels have remained roughly the same compared to last year which is not necessarily a good sign.

- The inventory holding period has decreased from 60.93 days to 30.55 days, which may indicate that the business is unable to buy further inventory and could mean that inventory may well run out.

Gearing has increased which means that the banks are happy to lend money to this business.

- There is an increase in the level of gearing from 26.33% to 43.17%.
- This is as a result of the significant bank overdraft the business now has.
- There has been a fall in the long term borrowing which may mean that banks are not happy to lend the company money over a long period.
- The increase in the bank overdraft has been used to fund the working capital of the business; there has been no investment in non-current assets.

Recommendation

The increase in credit limit should not be granted based on the performance indicators and financial information.

You would not recommend granting the increase in credit limit to Lily Limited.

(b) External sources of information include (**note** – only two are required):

Bank references – a request can be made about the credit worthiness of a potential customer. Limitations include:

- references are fairly standard and therefore must be interpreted
- banks will not be able to indicate how quickly a customer pays debts

Trade references – usually two references are sought from existing suppliers about the trading relationship, including credit terms and limits and if the customer pays on time. Limitations include:

- the customer may have selected the suppliers with whom they always pay on time
- the overall payment pattern to suppliers may not be reflected

Credit circles – a group of similar businesses who exchange information about customers, they are commonly members of a trade association. Limitations include:

- other businesses may be unwilling to provide information about their suppliers, as they may fear losing their customer
- the information may be inaccurate

Credit reference agencies – independent organisations that provide a credit rating checking service. Limitations include:

- there may be little or no information for new businesses
- any information available may be out of date

Other published sources – information may be available from a variety of sources, including the internet, trade publications and articles from the press. Limitations include:

- the information may be unreliable
- information may be historic and out of date

Task 4

(a) Sales revenue for 20-4 compared to 20-3 has increased by **12.02%** which means that the company may have **experienced an increased demand for its products.**

(b) The gross profit margin has remained constant, which indicates that the company has **made no change to the selling and purchase price of its product**.

(c) The company is making a **profit** at operational level and the operating profit margin has **increased**.

(d) The trade payables payment period measures on average the number of days that **the company takes to pay its suppliers**. For Weber Ltd this has **fallen** slightly.

(e) The current ratio is **greater than 1**, which is a **good sign**.

(f) The quick ratio is **more than 1** which **is not** a major concern in terms of liquidity.

(g) The inventory holding period has remained constant. This is a **good sign** and indicates **stability**.

(h) Overall it appears that the company is **solvent** and has **sufficient** liquidity to pays its liabilities as they fall due.

(i) On the basis of the financial statements that have been provided to us and the key performance indicators, I recommend that **credit be given** to Weber Ltd.

Workings:

(a) Increase in revenue (3,988 – 3,560) / 3,560 = 12.02%

	Formula	**20-4**	**20-3**
Gross profit margin %	$\dfrac{\text{Gross profit} \times 100}{\text{Sales revenue}}$	$\dfrac{2{,}431 \times 100}{3{,}998} = 60.96\%$	$\dfrac{2{,}136 \times 100}{3{,}560} = 60\%$
Trade payables pmt period in days	$\dfrac{\text{Trade payables} \times 365}{\text{Cost of sales}}$	$\dfrac{248 \times 365}{1{,}557} = 58.14$	$\dfrac{231 \times 365}{1{,}424} = 59.21$
Inventory holding period in days	$\dfrac{\text{Inventories} \times 365}{\text{Cost of sales}}$	$\dfrac{151 \times 365}{1{,}557} = 35.4$	$\dfrac{137 \times 365}{1{,}424} = 35.12$
Current ratio	$\dfrac{\text{Current assets}}{\text{Current liabilities}}$	$\dfrac{858}{248} = 3.46$	$\dfrac{808}{231} = 3.5$
Quick ratio	$\dfrac{\text{Current assets less inventories}}{\text{Current liabilities}}$	$\dfrac{858 - 151}{248} = 2.85$	$\dfrac{808 - 137}{231} = 2.9$

Task 5

(a)

Warrant of execution	→	An order for the court bailiffs to seize assets belonging to the customer who owes money to the seller
Warrant of delivery	→	An order for the court bailiffs to seize goods belonging to the seller and held by a customer who owes money to the seller
Attachment of earnings	→	An order which will authorise an employer to deduct regular amounts from the customer's salary in order to repay the debt

(b)   (b) is True; the remaining statements are False

(c)   Alexia Insurance is offering Credit insurance

The overall cost to Dashboard Ltd for the year is £7,000

Workings: ((£1,000 x 12) – £5,000)

(d)   (b)   Appointed by a bank under its floating charge and is authorised to sell the secured assets of the company in order to repay the bank borrowing in preference to unsecured trade payables

(e)   The 80/20 rule states that **20**% of customer accounts make up **80**% of the total value of outstanding debts.

The **average period of credit** indicates how long a customer takes to pay debts.

Slow paying customers can be highlighted by using the **aged receivables analysis**.

(f)   (c)   As there was no defined offer or acceptance there is unlikely to be a contract and so no remedies are likely to succeed

Task 6

(a)   (a) is False; the remaining statements are True

(b)   The simple annual interest rate of the discount is 24.83%

Workings:

$$\left(\frac{2}{98}\right) \times \left(\frac{365}{60-30}\right) \times 100 = 24.83\%$$

The compound annual interest rate of the discount is 27.86%

Workings:

$$\left\{\left(1 + \frac{2}{98}\right)^{\wedge\left(\frac{365}{60-30}\right)} - 1\right\} \times 100 = 27.86\%$$

(c)   (d)   The introduction of a factoring company to manage trade receivables

(d)   £77,700

Workings: (£78,000 x 25%) + (£80,000 x 75% x 97%)

(e)   (b)   2, 3 and 4 only

(f)   £10,479.58

Workings: £10,700 − (£10,700 x 0.0206)

Task 7

(a)   **Magnum Ltd**
- The account should have been put on stop because it is more than 28 days overdue.
- A member of staff should visit the premises of Magnum Ltd and ask for immediate payment.
- The debt should be placed in the hands of a debt collection agency if the visit proves to be unsuccessful.
- A claim of £9,100 should be made from the insurer (ie 70% of the net invoice amount).
- Once the debt is over six months old Bad Debt Relief of £2,600 should be claimed from HMRC.
- A provision of £3,900 should be made in the accounts.

Hudsons Inc
- Additional care must be taken with foreign customers as they may take longer to settle invoices and allowing them to exceed their credit limit would not be advisable.
- Hudsons Inc must be contacted and asked for settlement of the £25,000 before the new order of £35,000 can be processed.

Shoreline Ltd

- For the invoice dated 30 June 20-3 use the normal credit control process which will be a telephone call on 7 August 20-3 followed by a letter on 14 August 20-3.
- For the invoice dated 31 May 20-3 contact Shoreline Ltd and ask why the payment has not been made yet.
- As Shoreline Ltd usually pays on time it is possible that the older invoice is in dispute or that the payment has been lost or misposted.
- It is not necessary at this stage to make any provision in the accounts.

(b)   Balance at 30 June 20-3 = £72,000

Balance at 31 July 20-3 = £61,680

Note that the question asks for a calculation of the balances of the account at the end of the two months. This may either be carried out as a straight arithmetic exercise, or it can be done by completing two 'T' accounts as shown below.

Dr			**Sheila Mary Ltd**			Cr
		£				£
1 Jun	B/d	165,000				
8 Jun	Invoice	72,000	5 Jun	Bank		162,000
			6 Jun	Credit note		3,000
			30 Jun	C/d		72,000
		237,000				237,000

Dr			**Sheila Mary Ltd**			Cr
		£				£
1 Jul	B/d	72,000				
15 Jul	Invoice	67,200	17 Jul	Credit note		5,520
			20 Jul	Bank		72,000
			31 Jul	C/d		61,680
		139,200				139,200

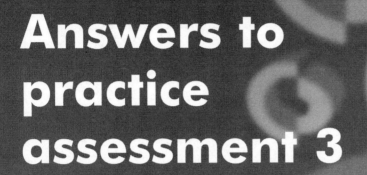

Answers to practice assessment 3

Task 1

(a) An acceptance of an offer must be **unconditional**.

An offer in contract law for the sale of goods may be terminated when **a counter offer is made**.

A person who sues for damages is someone who **takes legal action** in the courts for **money compensation for breach of contract**.

(b) £131.18   *Workings:* (£7,000 x 1.2) x (1.5% + 8%) x 60/365

(c) (a) and (c) are True; (b) and (d) are False

(d) (c)   £7,200 *Workings:* ((£600 x 40) – £16,800)

(e) (a)   The £5 is sufficient consideration even if a very low price is set as a favour to the buyer

   (a)   There is no valid contract because the agreement was a domestic one and not intended to create legal relations

Task 2

(a)

Garden Design Limited	20-2 Indicator	20-2 Rating	20-1 Indicator	20-1 Rating
Operating profit margin %	15	10	–4	–5
Interest cover	32.14	10	No cover	–30
Quick ratio	2.23	10	3.47	10
Gearing %	34.97	10	65.71	–20
Total credit rating		40		–45

Workings:

	Formula	20-2	20-1
Operating profit margin %	Profit from operations x 100 / Sales revenue	1,125 x 100 / 7,500 = 15%	252 x 100 / 6,300 = –4%
Interest cover	Profit from operations / Interest payable	1,125 / 35 = 32.14	No cover
Quick ratio	Current assets less inventories / Current liabilities	1,427 – 151 / 571 = 2.23	1,632 – 148 / 428 = 3.47
Gearing %	Total debt x 100 / Total debt plus equity	1,000 x 100 / 1,000 + 1,860 = 34.97%	1,600 x 100 / 1,600 + 835 = 65.71%

(b) (c) Request latest management accounts and defer decision

Task 3

(a) Profitability

The turnover has increased by 13% or £595,000. The increase is explained by the new contracts.

Gross profit has increased by £357,000 or 13%, which is in line with the percentage increase in turnover. The gross profit margin has remained constant at 60%.

The profit from operations has fallen and in 20-2 there is an operating loss. What is of concern is that whilst the gross profit margin has remained at 60%, the operating profit margin has fallen from 10.99% to –5.13%.

The administration expenses have increased from 37% of sales revenue to 53%, which has contributed to the operating loss. The significant increase in administration expenses can be explained by the writing off of the obsolete non-current assets in 20-2.

Interest cover was over 50 times in the previous year and now there is no cover, as the company no longer has any borrowing commitments which attract interest.

Liquidity

Generally, the higher the current ratio the better from an assessment of credit perspective. The current ratio is a crude measure of solvency and in this case it has increased from 4.38 in the previous year to 5.36, which is a positive sign.

The components of the current assets figure need to be looked at further to determine liquidity.

The cash balance has increased by £66,000, which is a positive sign.

Trade receivables have increased from £626,000 to £708,000, an increase would be expected with the increase in sales revenue. The collection period has remained constant which is a good sign.

Trade payables have decreased and the payment period has also decreased. This indicates that the company is moving towards paying suppliers more quickly.

Inventory levels have increased in line with the increase in cost of sales. The inventory holding period has decreased slightly from 53.05 days to 49.95, which is an indicator that inventory may be being used more efficiently.

Gearing

There is a decrease in gearing from 10.59% to nothing, which may be an indicator that the banks are no longer prepared to lend the business money. Alternatively, it may simply be that the business no longer has any borrowing requirements.

There has been a large change in equity with an injection of capital of £2.6 million. The capital appears to have funded the purchase of non-current assets and repayment of the long-term loan.

Financial Information

The financial statements supplied are over 18 months old, therefore the comments made are based on very historic information and up to date figures must be made available.

Recommendation

The increase in credit limit, which is four times the current limit, should not be granted based on the reluctance of Berry Limited to provide up-to-date financial information.

Berry Limited should be contacted and told that the decision has been deferred until the 20-3 financial statements have been supplied and analysed.

(b) A person who is objective will base their opinions on facts and must not be influenced by personal beliefs, feelings or others; this applies to all people working in a finance function.

Within credit control the correct organisational procedures must be followed at all times which includes:

- ensuring that up-to-date financial information is analysed before any increase in credit can be allowed

- seeking references before granting credit

- treating all customers fairly and equally

- chasing outstanding debts on time

- reporting any potential problems to the appropriate manager

The Sales Manager of Hollywood Limited has a conflict of interest as the Financial Director of Berry Limited is his brother in law, therefore his request for the immediate increase in credit limit should be declined and the correct procedures followed.

Task 4

(a) Sales revenue for 20-3 compared to 20-2 has increased by **35.01%**, which means that the company may have **either sold more units or increased the selling price of its product**.

(b) Gross profit has increased by **35.99%** and profit from operations has increased by **36.97%**. Both the gross profit margin and the operating profit margin have **increased** slightly.

(c) The current ratio provides a rough measure of the **short-term solvency** of the organisation. In the case of Joseph Ltd it has **fallen** and is now **less than 1**, which is a **sign of poor liquidity**.

(d) The inventory level has **decreased**; this is a **bad sign** as the inventory holding period has **decreased**, which may mean that **inventory could run out**.

(e) The quick ratio has **fallen** which **is** a major concern and indicates **poor** liquidity.

(f) The trade payables payment period has **increased** by **34.92** days. It appears that the company is **finding it more difficult** to pay its liabilities as they fall due.

(g) On the basis of the financial statements that have been provided to us and the key performance indicators I recommend that **credit not be given** to Joseph Limited.

Workings:

(a) Increase in revenue (6,124 – 4,536) / 4,536 = 35.01%

(b) Increase in gross profit (1,840 – 1,353) / 1,353 = 35.99%

(b) Increase in profit from operations (615 – 449) / 449 = 36.97%

(f) Increase in trade payables payment days 90.99 – 56.07 = 34.92 days

	Formula	20-3	20-2
Gross profit margin %	$\dfrac{\text{Gross profit} \times 100}{\text{Sales revenue}}$	$\dfrac{1,840 \times 100}{6,124} = 30.05\%$	$\dfrac{1,353 \times 100}{4,536} = 29.83\%$
Operating profit margin %	$\dfrac{\text{Profit from operations} \times 100}{\text{Sales revenue}}$	$\dfrac{615 \times 100}{6,124} = 10.04\%$	$\dfrac{449 \times 100}{4,536} = 9.9\%$
Trade payables pmt period in days	$\dfrac{\text{Trade payables} \times 365}{\text{Cost of sales}}$	$\dfrac{1,068 \times 365}{4,284} = 90.99$	$\dfrac{489 \times 365}{3,183} = 56.07$
Inventory holding period in days	$\dfrac{\text{Inventories} \times 365}{\text{Cost of sales}}$	$\dfrac{328 \times 365}{4,284} = 27.95$	$\dfrac{392 \times 365}{3,183} = 44.95$
Current ratio	$\dfrac{\text{Current assets}}{\text{Current liabilities}}$	$\dfrac{1,012}{56 + 1,068} = 0.9$	$\dfrac{854}{489} = 1.75$
Quick ratio	$\dfrac{\text{Current assets less inventories}}{\text{Current liabilities}}$	$\dfrac{1,012 - 328}{56 + 1,068} = 0.61$	$\dfrac{854 - 392}{489} = 0.94$

Task 5

(a)

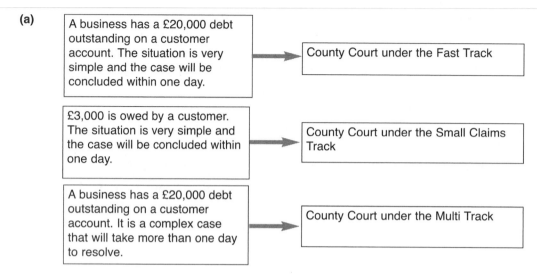

(b)   (a) and (c) are True; (b) and (d) are False

(c)   Trade Finance is offering: Invoice discounting

Maiden Ltd can borrow: £402,400

Workings: £503,000 x 80%

(d)   (b) A conflict of interest

(e)   **Clarke Ltd** has one invoice dated 14 September 20-3, a final reminder is being sent to the customer.

The balance for **Rhodes Ltd** relates to a credit note for a prompt payment discount created by Austen Ltd in error.

The account for **Stein Ltd** is not overdue and no action needs to be taken at present.

Day Ltd has gone into administration; VAT will be reclaimed from HMRC as the correct conditions have been met.

(f)   (a)   £5,000

Task 6

(a) **Grimshaw Ltd**

Contact the credit insurer to make a claim for **£0**, make a provision for **£15,000** and claim VAT of **£3,000** from HMRC.

(b) The simple annual interest rate of the discount is 40.69%

Workings:

$$\left(\frac{2.5}{97.5}\right) \times \left(\frac{365}{30-7}\right) \times 100 = 40.69\%$$

The compound annual interest rate of the discount is 49.45%

Workings:

$$\left\{\left(1+\frac{2.5}{97.5}\right)^{\wedge\left(\frac{365}{30-7}\right)} -1\right\} \times 100 = 49.45\%$$

(c) (c) Try to recover the money and hope that the company recovers

(d) £5,100

Workings: (£146,000 + £154,000) x 85% x 2%

(e) (b) Non-recourse factoring

(f) The receivables collection period (to the nearest day) is **41** days.

Workings: (£112,500 / [£44 x 23,010]) x 365

Task 7

(a)   **Beck Ltd**

- Ensure that the account has been put on stop.
- Establish why Beck Ltd is refusing to pay.
- Establish if Beck Ltd still has the goods to which this debt relates and if so reclaim them under the retention of title clause.
- Consider taking legal action if the goods cannot be identified.
- Make a provision in the accounts for £750.
- Make a claim with the insurers for £1,750.
- Claim £500 back from HMRC when the debt is over six months old.

Free Ltd

- The products which have been manufactured by Opto Ltd have a batch number, therefore they should be separately identifiable from other products.
- A member of staff should visit the premises of Free Ltd to identify the products supplied in the presence of the receiver.
- A claim should be made from the insurer for £8,750.
- The VAT of £2,500 is reclaimable from HMRC.
- A provision of £3,750 should be made in the accounts.

Hardy Ltd

- The premises of Hardy Ltd should be visited to establish whether or not the company is still trading.
- A provision should be made in the accounts for the full amount of the debt less VAT as the debt will not be credit insured.
- VAT can be reclaimed from HMRC.
- A debt collection company should be engaged to pursue the matter further.

(b)   **Monte Ltd**

Balance at 31 May 20-3 = £36,800
Workings: [105,000 + (40,000 x 1.2) − (18,000 x 90%) − 100,000 = 36,800]

Balance at 30 June 20-3 = £80,000
Workings: [36,800 − 30,000 + 78,000 − 4,800 = 80,000]

Note: T-accounts are also shown as possible workings below.

Dr			**Monte Ltd**			Cr
		£				£
1 May	B/d	105,000				
8 May	Invoice	48,000	10 May	Credit note		16,200
			10 May	Bank		100,000
			31 May	C/d		36,800
		153,000				153,000

Dr		**Monte Ltd**			Cr
		£			£
1 Jun	B/d	36,800			
16 Jun	Invoice	78,000	10 Jun	Bank	30,000
			26 Jun	Credit note	4,800
			30 Jun	C/d	80,000
		114,800			114,800

for your notes

for your notes

for your notes

for your notes

for your notes

for your notes

for your notes

for your notes

for your notes

for your notes

for your notes